Scholastic
Literacy
Skills

C000147649

Grammar and punctuation

AGES 9–10

TERM-BY-TERM PHOTOCOPIABLES

AUTHOR HUW THOMAS

EDITOR STEVEN CARRUTHERS

ASSISTANT EDITOR ROANNE DAVIS

SERIES DESIGNER CLAIRE BELCHER

DESIGNER SARAH ROCK

ILLUSTRATIONS TERRY McKENNA

Designed using Adobe Pagemaker

Published by Scholastic Ltd, Villiers House, Clarendon Avenue, Leamington Spa, Warwickshire CV32 5PR
Text © Huw Thomas

© 1999 Scholastic Ltd

1 2 3 4 5 6 7 8 9 0   9 0 1 2 3 4 5 6

British Library Cataloguing-in-Publication Data
A catalogue record for this book is available from the British Library.

ISBN 0-590-63664-2

Acknowledgements
The publishers gratefully acknowledge permission to reproduce the following copyright material:
❑ Faber & Faber for the use of extracts from *The Ghost Drum* by Susan Hill © 1989, Susan Hill (1989, Faber & Faber) and 'The Great Querne' from *The Rollickers and Other Stories* by Andrew Gibson © 1992, Andrew Gibson (1992, Faber & Faber).
❑ Pavilion Books for the use of 'Three Raindrops' from *Fairy Tales* by Terry Jones © 1997, Terry Jones (1997, Pavilion Books).
❑ Penguin Books Ltd for the use of extracts from *Kaspar in the Glitter* by Philip Ridley © 1994, Philip Ridley (1994, Viking) and an extract from *Something Else* by Kathryn Cave © 1994, Kathryn Cave (1994, Viking).
❑ The Peters Fraser and Dunlop Group Limited on behalf of Michael Rosen for the use of 'Pop' from *You Tell Me* by Michael Rosen © 1981, Michael Rosen (1981, Puffin).
❑ Routledge for the use of two poems from *Knots* by R.D. Laing © 1969, R.D. Laing (1969, Tavistock Publications).
❑ Scholastic Children's Books for the use of 'Don't' from *Don't Put Mustard In The Custard* by Michael Rosen © 1996, Michael Rosen (1996, André Deutsch).uotes from the back of *Granny* by Anthony Horowitz © 1995, Walker Books Ltd (1995, Walker Books).

Every effort has been made to trace copyright holders for the works reproduced in this book, and the publishers apologize for any inadvertent omissions.

Contents

Introduction

Welcome to grammar and punctuation

'As a writer I know that I must select studiously the nouns, pronouns, verbs, adverbs, etcetera, and by a careful syntactical arrangement make readers laugh, reflect or riot.'

Maya Angelou

The *Scholastic Literacy Skills: Grammar and punctuation* series equips teachers with resources and subject training enabling them to teach grammar and punctuation at Key Stage 2. The focus of the resource is on what is sometimes called *sentence-level* work, so called because grammar and punctuation primarily involve the construction and understanding of sentences.

Many teachers approach the teaching of grammar bringing with them a lot of past memories. Some will remember school grammar lessons as the driest of subjects, involving drills and parsing, and will wonder how they can make it exciting for their own class. At the other end of the spectrum, some will have received relatively little formal teaching of grammar at school. Recent research by the Qualifications and Curriculum Authority found a lack of confidence among Key Stage 2 teachers when it came to teaching sentence structure, commenting that:

'Where teachers were less confident, it tended to be because sentence structure had not formed part of their own education.'

(QCA, 1998, page 28)

In other words there are teachers who, when asked to teach clause structure or prepositions, feel at a bit of a loss. They are being asked to teach things they are not confident with themselves. Even worse, they think they should be confident in these things.

Grammar can evoke lethargy, fear, irritation, pedantry and despondency. Yet at the beginning of this introduction we have one of the greatest modern writers presenting her crafting of sentences as an exciting and tactical process that has a powerful effect on her readers. Can this be the grammar that makes teachers squirm or run?

The *Scholastic Literacy Skills: Grammar and punctuation* series

The *Scholastic Literacy Skills: Grammar and punctuation* series works from the premise that grammar and punctuation can be interesting and dynamic – but on one condition. The condition is that the teaching of these aspects of grammar must be related to *real texts* and *practical activities* that experiment with language, investigate the use of language in real contexts and find the ways in which grammar and punctuation are used in our day-to-day talk, writing and reading. The series is based upon five principles about the teaching of grammar:

1. Meaningful sentence-level work
In looking at how sentences are put together in a text, an appreciation of the function of that text is crucial. As children investigate the structure of sentences or the types of words they contain, they need to be aware of them as communicative acts; the purposes of the various pieces of writing considered in this resource play a crucial role in the activities. As children work through various aspects of *Grammar and punctuation*, teachers should reflect on how individual children are using their developing understanding of sentences in the rest of their written and spoken work.

2. Language from real life
As far as is possible, children need to work with language set in real-life contexts rather than always looking at contrived texts and exercises. Instead of made-up newspapers, for example, they need to look at extracts from the real thing. They need the encouragement to look at language in their environment, the books they enjoy and the things they and their peers say to one another. These are some of the most valuable resources available for language work because in using them children will apply what they learn to texts they know.

Introduction

The *Scholastic Literacy Skills: Grammar and punctuation* series does contain a number of exercises in which sentences have been constructed purely to provide examples of the use of a particular type of word or punctuation mark. However, this is always complemented by more realistic uses of language. The aim is consistently to refer children to genuine texts extracted from real books and actual newspapers. For this reason the *Scholastic Literacy Skills: Grammar and punctuation* series asks children to work on grammar and punctuation using texts as diverse as fables, jokes, book blurbs, leaflets, children's own writing, comic stories, poems, scripts, comedy sketches, labels, classic poetry, texts in various dialects… in fact the mix is as rich and lively as the children's own language experiences should be. A flick through the photocopiable material in this book will show the commitment of the series to varied and interesting texts based on the conviction that relevant and appropriate texts will motivate children to learn about language.

3. Teachers as active participants

The 'rules' of grammar and punctuation are not static aspects of language; we are all continually revising and developing them. The most competent and experienced of writers can still find new and interesting features of these aspects of language and develop their own use of English. Because of this the *Scholastic Literacy Skills: Grammar and punctuation* series equips the teacher with subject knowledge, definitions and explanations as

preparation for the subject matter of each unit. It is important that, as far as is possible, teachers join in with activities. If, for example, an activity involves bringing a leaflet in from home and looking at the use of persuasive language, then everyone should take part. What many teachers have found is that grammar and punctuation can be great levellers. In other words, as children investigate these aspects of language, the teacher can join in and genuinely participate in developing his or her own use of English.

4. Structure is essential

While the *Scholastic Literacy Skills: Grammar and punctuation* series is full of interesting and lively material, it is underpinned by a clear and deliberate structure. The sentence-level aspects of English are so many and so varied that teaching them effectively demands a structured approach. The basic aim has been to provide a clearly structured resource that uses common sense and introduces features such as sentence structure and punctuation in ways that build continuity and progression into children's learning.

The half-term sections and units of each book are structured in a way that develops the teaching of grammar and punctuation in Key Stage 2 in England, Wales and Northern Ireland, and Levels C–E in Scotland. Care has been taken to encompass the National Literacy Strategy *Framework for Teaching* (DfEE, 1998), so that teachers following the strategy can use these books with the confidence that they are delivering all the appropriate sentence-level objectives for each year group.

5. Active enjoyment

This is not a book of basic drills. The *Scholastic Literacy Skills: Grammar and punctuation* series was put together in the knowledge that grammar and punctuation *can* be taught in a dry and dull way but with a commitment to do the complete opposite. With this in mind, the activities are constructed in a way that involves a lot of active investigative work and play with language.

The books provide a balanced 'diet' of exercises mixed with practical, hands-on activities, including researching language, recording and analysing speech, drama activities, games and advertising. The underlying premise is that language is interesting, that understanding it can be fascinating and that working with it can be fun.

Grammar and punctuation: do they matter?

Any introduction to the teaching of grammar and punctuation sets up a stall in the middle of one of the hottest debates in the teaching of English. For this reason it is necessary to say a few things about the usefulness and purpose of sentence-level teaching.

Background

There was a period from the 1960s to the 1980s when the teaching of grammar in particular and punctuation to a lesser extent was not in vogue. This was, in part, due to research projects in the 1960s that claimed to have shown the teaching of such aspects of English to be 'useless' and even 'harmful' (for example, Harris's research summarized in QCA, 1998). The Kingman Report in 1988 marked a change in this situation. After a period in which grammar had lain dormant, this report promoted the use of grammatical terminology in relevant contexts and recommended that all trainee teachers receive a large amount of 'direct tuition of knowledge about language' (HMSO, 1988, page 69).

A large portion of the Kingman Report was devoted to considering the talk and work of children. These were examined and the implicit linguistic knowledge in these activities was drawn out, such as the six-year-old whose writing demonstrated implicit understanding of subordinate clauses and qualifying phrases (HMSO, 1988, page 36). Taking the example of discussion about pronouns they made a comment that:

'Since… teacher and pupil need, in discussion, a word which refers to a class of terms (i.e. pronouns) there is no good reason not to use that term.'

(HMSO, 1988, page 13)

What Kingman raised was the usefulness of knowledge about language in the teaching of English.

Reasons for teaching grammar and punctuation

Grammar and punctuation are sometimes seen as symbols of a golden age when children were taught 'the basics'. This sort of talk has not served the subject well. It took some time for the Kingman recommendations to permeate into the English curriculum in a thorough and progressive way. It is crucial that, as teachers embark on the teaching of grammar and punctuation, they do so with a clear sense of exactly what it is these subjects will provide the learner with. The *Scholastic Literacy Skills: Grammar and punctuation* series is based on the following theoretical understanding of the value of teaching grammar and punctuation.

❑ Understanding and using terminology used to describe aspects of grammar and punctuation equips children with the vocabulary they need to discuss language. For example, it can be much easier to discuss the ambiguities that can surround the use of pronouns with children if they understand the term 'pronoun' and are beginning to use it to describe some of the words they use.

❑ Looking at aspects of sentence construction stimulates children to reflect on their own use of language. For example, many teachers try to discourage the overuse of the word 'and…' as in 'I went out and I saw my friend and we played in the park and we went to the shop and we bought…' and so on. Guiding children out of this overuse of 'and' is a task with which many teachers are familiar. It can be greatly enhanced by an understanding of certain aspects of grammar and punctuation such as how sentences break up a piece of writing so that it makes sense; other words and terms that can connect sentences and clauses together; ways in which sentences and clauses can be punctuated; and the functions performed by specific connecting words and phrases.

❑ There are links within the subject of English that make one aspect vital to the understanding of another. For example, the understanding of how certain texts address and persuade their readers involves an awareness of the concept of 'person' in pronouns and verbs. Another example is the way in which the use of the comma can depend on an understanding of how clauses function. Many aspects of grammar and punctuation play vital roles in other areas of English.

❑ Grammar and punctuation can provide a means of evaluating how effectively and clearly a spoken or written piece of language communicates. For example, the teacher who is exasperated by a child's constant use of the word 'nice' to describe everything he or she likes might find some work on adjectives steers the child towards new ways of describing.

❑ An appreciation of grammar and punctuation empowers children to make full use of the English language. Starting with simple sentences, children can move on to an understanding of features such as nouns, verbs, commas, clauses, adjectives and adverbs. Grammar and punctuation become the tools that enable children to explore new ways of expressing themselves in their writing.

Introduction

❏ Linguistics, the study of language, is a subject in its own right. Looking at grammar and punctuation gives children their first encounters with this fascinating subject. The discussion of language features such as dialect words and expressions introduces children to the subject of sociolinguistics. This is the study of how language functions within society and it is just one example of the way in which the study of language can be an interesting subject in itself.

Working with *Scholastic Literacy Skills: Grammar and punctuation*

Unit structure

Each book in the *Scholastic Literacy Skills: Grammar and punctuation* series is broken up into six sections, each of which is structured to provide resources for a half-term. Within each section, material is gathered together to give a specific content to that half-term, indicated on the contents page. Each section contains two 'posters' that present some of the material covered over the half-term in an accessible form for reference. These are so named because it is recommended that they are enlarged to A3 size (or A2, using two A3 sheets) and placed on display while the units are undertaken. They can also be used as shared texts in reading activities as well as posters provided for reference in the classroom.

Each half-term section is split into five units, each dealing with a specific aspect of grammar or punctuation. Within each unit there are three photocopiables. These are prefaced by introductory material, structured under the following headings:

Objective: the learning objective(s) for the unit.
Language issues: explanatory material on the issues covered in the unit. These are predominantly focused on the subject matter of the unit and can provide clarification for the teacher, equipping him or her towards delivery of the unit.
Ways of teaching: notes on the teaching of the subject matter. This section can provide specific points about the approach to be adopted and the terminology to be used, and has a specific bearing upon the teaching of the unit.
About the activities: a note that clarifies any information the teacher may need for the unit. In some cases this is a full explanation of the activity; in others it is just a hint on the presentation of the subject matter.
Following up: optional activity suggestions to follow up the content of the unit. These can be specific activities but they can also be notes as to how the content of the unit can dovetail with other aspects of English.

Differentiation

The activities in each book are produced with the average ability of the relevant year group in mind. They draw upon the work of the National Literacy Project, a pilot project that led to the production of the National Literacy Strategy (DfEE, 1998). Differentiation should be possible within each unit in the following ways:

❏ *Providing support* in the way activities are staged. When, for example, there are three stages to an activity, the teacher can assist children who need support through one or more of the stages.

❏ *Reducing the amount of material.* If an activity asks children to complete a certain number of tasks, such as the ordering of ten mixed-up sentences, the teacher may reduce the number for a child needing such support.

❏ *Pre-selecting appropriate material* for investigative tasks. Many of the units ask children to find texts or try activities with sentences they find in the classroom. In such cases the teacher could direct children who would find this difficult to specified sentences or previously selected material.

❏ *Providing follow-up work.* More able children can benefit from being given one of the tasks under the heading 'Following up', extending their work based on the objective of the unit.

A 'resource', not a 'scheme'

The photocopiables in each book are a support for teaching. While they may carry notes to inform children, the actual teaching of the learning objective can only be achieved through discussion of the language issues supported by the use of the photocopiable sections. This takes us back to the idea of the teacher as an active participant. These materials are to be used by the class working in conjunction with the teacher and should support the teacher's explanation and discussion of the subject matter in each unit.

It should be stressed that *Scholastic Literacy Skills: Grammar and punctuation* does not intend to provide a scheme that children slavishly work their way through. It is a flexible teaching resource. While each book provides the subject matter appropriate to the age group at which it is aimed, the teacher will soon realize there is more material in each book than a class could be expected to cover in one year. The introductory pages at the start of each half-termly section and the language issues sections are there to enable teachers to select the photocopiable

page, poster, or activity from the 'Following up' section, that best supports their own planning, the needs of the class – and personal preferences.

Texts, texts and more texts!

Various activities call for a range of resources. Check each activity to see what is needed in the way of paper, scissors, glue and so on. The most valuable resource, however, is a rich variety of texts available for the children's use – collect together a truly mixed bag of old and new texts (familiar and unfamiliar), including leaflets, menus, newspapers, comics, letters, junk mail, posters… the broader the range the better!

Introduction to Ages 9–10

The thirty units comprising *Scholastic Literacy Skills: Grammar and punctuation, Ages 9-10* have as their objective to revisit and to extend children's understanding of various aspects of sentence structure, including the use of verbs, clauses, pronouns and prepositions.

The main progression in this year is the introduction of units that call for more reflection upon the way sentences influence their readers. In particular, aspects of grammar are examined as a way of discerning how clearly – or ambiguously – a sentence can work. There is also a move towards more complex and carefully structured sentences. This development needs to be handled with care. No-one is suggesting that a long and complex sentence is a

better or more competent use of English. However, an understanding of the different types of clause, as well as the punctuation of more complex sentences, will afford children access to a wider repertoire of means of expression in their writing work.

There is a clear emphasis upon the use of texts to develop children's understanding of these elements in context. This is particularly important as children develop their initial ideas of what constitutes the various parts of speech.

For this age group, children are also encouraged to understand some conventions of standard English (such as the way in which dialogue is set out, and the difference between direct and reported speech). The differences between written and spoken English are also investigated.

Verbs

Contents of Term 1a

This half-term

Verbs are those all important words that are needed in the vast majority of sentences. In this half-term children extend their understanding of verbs through units that examine the form and person of verbs. There is also an introduction to auxiliary verbs. This is crucial because some of the verbs children are most familiar with, such as 'can' and 'do', are auxiliaries.

Poster notes

Words that make auxiliary verbs
This poster presents a few of the words that function as auxiliary verbs with examples of this function. As such it supports each of the units on auxiliaries. It should be stressed that these are a few examples and that, in the units, other auxiliaries are encountered.

Sentence types
The examples used in this poster feature in Unit 4. The poster presents the four types of sentence.

Words that make auxiliary verbs

FOR EXAMPLE

She is riding her bike.

The weather is turning gloomy.

IS

FOR EXAMPLE

Don't walk on the grass!

I don't like Mondays.

DON'T

FOR EXAMPLE

I can ride a bike.

The dog can jump onto the wall.

CAN

FOR EXAMPLE

I should tell my mum where I'm going.

You should wipe your feet.

SHOULD

FOR EXAMPLE

I might help my friend.

The door might slam.

MIGHT

FOR EXAMPLE

I must remember my homework.

Sam must go to the dentist.

MUST

Sentence types

DECLARATIVE

Definition:
Sentences that state something.

INTERROGATIVE

Definition:
Asks something.

IMPERATIVE

Definition:
Gives an order.

EXCLAMATORY

Definition:
**Exclaims! Sounds surprised!
An outburst!**

Scholastic Literacy Skills
Grammar and punctuation

Verbs

Objective
Revise work on verbs

Language issues
Verbs are words that denote an action or happening in a sentence. They can be active, denoting an action actively done *by* someone or something – for example, 'The boy kicked the ball through the window', or 'The wind blew the tree over' – or passive, denoting an action done *to* someone or something – for example, 'The ball was kicked through the window' or 'The tree was blown over by the wind'.

The subject of a verb is sometimes called the 'agent'. This denotes the person or thing that performs the action, so in both the 'blown' and 'blew' examples above the wind is the subject of the verb.

Ways of teaching
The activities in this unit revise the idea of a verb and look at the tenses and subjects of various verbs. The terms 'subject' and 'tense' are used in the activities and the teacher is encouraged to use them with the class.

About the activities
Photocopiable: Odd happenings
The odd occurrences in these text extracts provide interesting settings for unusual happenings, such as a person barking and a cat telling stories. These are analysed as children look at the verbs. The activity can begin with the children reading the texts and circling the verbs they encounter before completing the table.

Photocopiable: Changing tenses
As children remodel language from one tense to another two useful strategies are, firstly to say the sentence aloud and remodel it in speech before writing it down; and secondly, it helps if they think of the present tense sentence as happening *today* and the past tense sentence as happening *yesterday*. These words tend to provide a useful way of focusing the language in the past or present.

Photocopiable: Verb table
The analysis of verbs encouraged by this table should lead to some interesting readings of various texts. Encourage children to move beyond the example sentences to other sentences from various texts, such as stories or their own writing. In some cases the subject may not be mentioned in the sentence; for example,

games instructions ask the player to 'Roll the dice' but do not name the subject. Faced with such examples children would have to infer who does the rolling or leave the space blank.

Following up
Look at other passages: Children can collect cuttings from newspapers and magazines and read through them, circling the various verbs they find. They can look at the tenses of the verbs and determine if a particular tense dominates the text.

Tense ping-pong: As a way of revisiting tenses children can say sentences that describe what they are doing today beginning with the words 'Today I...'. They can then recreate those sentences in the past tense, beginning 'Yesterday I...'. This is a good activity to try with a partner. One child begins the activity with a 'Today I...' sentence which their partner has to remodel beginning 'Yesterday I...'.

Photographic verbs: Children can look at pictures of various actions or events in a newspaper and summarize each picture in a sentence. They can then look at the sentence to see if they can locate the verb and the subject.

Odd happenings

❑ Look at these extracts from two stories. They present odd scenes and odd happenings. Find some verbs in each passage. Record the action in each verb and who or what is performing the action (the subject).

From Kasper and the Glitter
by Philip Ridley

'WOOF!' went a voice.
The dogs stopped in their tracks.
Knucklehead had entered the kitchen.
He was holding the bones that had
been in the pram.
Slowly, Knucklehead went over to the
dogs and said, 'Woof!' once again. This
time in a gentler voice.
The dogs went back to their places by
the oven.
Knucklehead divided the bones
between them, then uttered three
'Woofs' in quick succession and the
dogs started to eat.

verb	subject
went	a voice

From The Ghost Drum *by Susan Price*

In a place far distant from where
you are now grows an oak-tree by a
lake.
Round the oak's trunk is a chain of
golden links.
Tethered to the chain is a learned
cat, and this most learned of all cats
walks round and round the tree
continually.
As it walks one way, it sings songs.
As it walks the other, it tells stories.

verb	subject

Changing tenses

❏ Look at these sentences written in the present tense. Change them to the past tense.

Present tense	Past tense
I run and kick the ball.	
You sing and we ask you to stop.	
He wears scruffy shoes and trips over the laces.	
I pour the juice and drink it slowly.	
We make a den, paint a sign and hang it on the door.	
My aunty climbs the ladder and clears the gutter.	
My dad cooks pancakes and tosses them in the air.	
The pilot flies the plane and lands it at the airport.	

Verb table

This table asks for some information about verbs.
❑ Try it out using these example sentences:

> *Moira threw the ball and broke the window.*

> *The driver stops the bus and the people get off it.*

❑ Find some other sentences and use the table to figure things out about the verbs.

Subject Who is doing the action or to whom is the action happening?	Verb What is the action or happening?	Tense Is it happening in the past, present or future?

Auxiliary verbs

Objective
Understand the term 'auxiliary verb'

Language issues
Auxiliary verbs are sometimes called 'helping' verbs. They act as auxiliaries to other verbs. They can make the main verb in a phrase *conditional*. For example, a sentence like 'I play Ludo' describes an action I actually do. An auxiliary verb like 'can' slots into the sentence to make 'I can play Ludo'. This sentence says that I can play it (I am able to), not that I necessarily do.

The verbs known as the primary verbs ('be', 'have', and 'do') can be main verbs:

I am cold
I have a cold
I did nothing.

or auxiliary verbs:

I was making a cake
I have told you once
I didn't see you.

'Used to', 'ought', 'need' and 'dare' can be used as auxiliaries or as verbs on their own – for example, 'I need a drink' or 'I need to drink a drink'.

The other auxiliary verbs, the modal verbs, are 'can', 'could', 'may', 'might', 'must', 'will', 'shall', 'would' and 'should'. They always act as auxiliaries to other verbs, such as 'I can run'. Auxiliaries can take the 'n't' contraction to make verbs like 'haven't', 'wasn't' and 'can't'.

Ways of teaching
Auxiliaries act in support of main verbs. As children encounter auxiliaries this difference needs to be borne in mind. The emphasis in this unit is upon perceiving the difference between main and auxiliary verbs.

About the activities
Photocopiable: Using auxiliary verbs
This activity prompts children to think about instances in which they would use particular verbs. In order to increase the challenge of the activity, the children could try and create a sentence with more than one auxiliary verb.

Photocopiable: Find the auxiliary
By picking apart the quotes from speech children locate the various auxiliaries. The activity supports the task of differentiating between main verbs and auxiliaries.

Photocopiable: Auxiliary charting
Taking what they have learned about auxiliary verbs, this activity begins with examples on the page and extends into looking for examples in other texts.

Following up
Listing: Before showing children the range of auxiliary verbs they can try to figure out the list for themselves, attempting to list all the auxiliary verbs they know, with examples of sentences using them.

Auxiliary setting: Children can write sentences using auxiliary verbs on slips of paper and present them to a partner who has to decide which is the main verb and which are the auxiliaries.

Listen: Listening to the conversation of adults, children can try locating examples of auxiliary verbs in use. This could extend to a challenge to decide which auxiliary verb is the most commonly used.

Using auxiliary verbs

❏ Make up a sentence using each of the auxiliary verbs below.

might	
could	
won't	
didn't	
has	
isn't	
are	
can't	
can	
must	

Find the auxiliary

❑ Look at the voice bubbles below. Find the auxiliary verbs. Circle the main verbs in one colour, and the auxiliary verbs in a different colour.

It won't work!

You don't own the park!

I was told a good joke today.

I am writing a story.

I didn't think it would snow.

The rain has stopped.

I can swim, can't I?

You must change your socks.

We are going to play basketball and you can join us.

Sam will open the window.

Have you heard this joke?

I can see where you hid the key.

The tap is leaking but Mum can fix it.

We must run to the cinema because the film has started.

I might leave my pudding.

I didn't know you were hiding in the basket.

I am so happy I could sing.

I may cook some pancakes – then again I might not.

Josh isn't coming to the party.

Auxiliary charting

❏ Beginning with the sentences in the examples, complete the auxiliary chart below.

You may be right.

I can't stand the smell of ketchup.

Would you prefer coffee or tea?

❏ Find examples of auxiliary verbs in use and record the auxiliary with the main verb it is helping. Look in other texts for auxiliary verbs and place them on the chart.

Sentence	Main verb	Auxiliary verb
You may be right.	be	may

Investigating auxiliary verbs

Objective
Use auxiliary verbs

Language issues
Auxiliary verbs change the main verb they modify in various ways. They can inject a note of conditionality into a verb phrase, as when 'I saved my money' becomes 'I should have saved my money'. They can also denote that something has happened or is happening – for example, 'The storm has passed' and 'The storm is passing'.

Modal verbs indicate the conditions of a main verb. For example, the sentence 'I eat food' is a plain statement of action. Modal verbs can give permission or show ability, as in 'I may eat food' or 'I can eat food'. They can also show the likelihood of the main verb. The sentence 'I will eat food' is a clear statement of an action with a strong likelihood of happening, whereas 'I might eat food' sounds less likely.

The modal verb is one of the ways in which auxiliary verbs are used to create the 'future tense' of English. Future tense verbs are never created on their own, as main verbs. The actions or happenings described by future tense verbs are conditional, however likely or unlikely they may be. The last two 'eat food' examples above both describe a future event using different

modals coupled with the simple form of the main verb. Each modal describes this future event with a different degree of probability.

Ways of teaching
The focus of this unit is the way in which the auxiliary verbs concerned modify the main verbs in the sentences. As they engage in the activities children should be encouraged to consider the change the auxiliary makes to the main verb.

About the activities
Photocopiable: Definite or not?
Through looking at these phrases children see the way in which auxiliary verbs can make a verb uncertain or conditional or can indicate that something is happening or has happened. As they read the sentences encourage them to ask whether the action or event described in the main verb is definite or indefinite.

Photocopiable: Insert an auxiliary
The sentences in this activity can be modified by particular auxiliaries. The children can use the full set of strips and auxiliaries and try swapping them around until they complete all the sentences.

Photocopiable: 'Don't'
By reading Rosen's play on the auxiliary verb 'don't', children can be encouraged to find their own examples of auxiliaries with which they can play. Once they have chosen their auxiliary verb or verb phrase encourage them to think of real examples where the verb is used and create ridiculous examples.

Following up
Probability: Starting with a set future event, children can write sentences about it using a modal verb that indicates the likelihood of the event occurring. Events such as 'The classroom door opening before playtime', 'Rain before home time' or 'United winning the cup' can provide a starting point. Children can create 'might', 'will' or 'won't' sentences depending on what they judge to be the likelihood of the event occurring.

Predictions: Children can write their own predictions and give them a score out of ten. They can give ten to a sentence that is definitely going to happen, zero to one that won't. They then have to judge any sentence that lies between these two poles.

Definite or not?

❑ Look at the sentences in the boxes below.
Some describe things that definitely did or did not happen. They are quite definite!

Some are not definite.
They describe things that might have happened or could happen in the future.

❑ Cut out the rectangles and sort the definite verbs from the not definite.

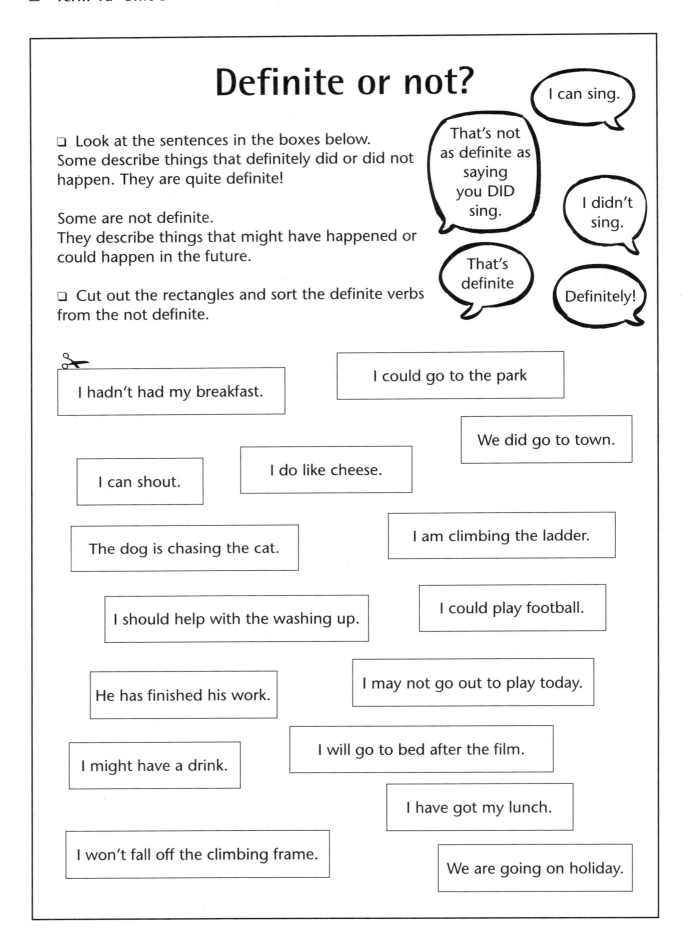

I hadn't had my breakfast.

I could go to the park

We did go to town.

I can shout.

I do like cheese.

The dog is chasing the cat.

I am climbing the ladder.

I should help with the washing up.

I could play football.

He has finished his work.

I may not go out to play today.

I might have a drink.

I will go to bed after the film.

I have got my lunch.

I won't fall off the climbing frame.

We are going on holiday.

Insert an auxiliary

The two parts of the sentences in the strips below need verbs to finish them.
❑ Using the verbs from the bottom of the page, complete the sentences.

I _____ painting the wall.

I _____ caught a cold.

I _____ got any money left in my money box.

Our _____ teachers playing football.

My mum _____ going to work.

Please _____ run on the stairs.

If it's sunny we _____ play outside.

My friend _____ run very fast.

After play we _____ go to the classroom.

My mum says I _____ stay away from the railway track.

On Saturday it _____ rain.

My Uncle _____ bought a motorbike.

am	are	is	have	has	haven't
don't	can	could	will	should	could

'Don't'

❑ Read the poem. It plays with the auxiliary verb 'don't'.

❑ Could you make up a poem playing with a different auxiliary?
It could be a list of things you could do (for example, 'I could eat a horse', 'I could become an astronaut'). It could be as daft as you want. It could be things you will do. It could be things you would like to do. It could be things you wouldn't like to do.

❑ Choose an auxiliary verb and play with some of the strange and unusual sentences it conjures up.

Don't
Don't do,
Don't do,
Don't do that.
Don't pull faces,
Don't tease the cat.

Don't pick your ears,
Don't be rude at school.
Who do they think I am?

Some kind of fool?

One day
they'll say
Don't put toffee in my coffee
don't pour gravy on the baby
don't put beer in his ear
don't stick your toes up his nose.

Don't put confetti on the spaghetti
and don't squash peas on your knees.

Don't put ants in your pants
don't put mustard in the custard

don't chuck jelly at the telly

and don't throw fruit at the computer
don't throw fruit at the computer.

Don't what?
Don't throw fruit at the computer.
Don't what?
Don't throw fruit at the computer.
What do they think I am?
Some kind of fool?

Michael Rosen

Verb forms

Objective
Examine the forms of verbs in different types of sentence

Language issues
There are four basic types of sentence:

❑ *Declarative* sentences make a statement – for example, 'The car is slow'.

❑ *Interrogative* sentences ask a question or are phrased in a questioning way – 'Is the car slow?' or 'The car is slow?'

❑ *Imperative* sentences issue commands and orders – 'Slow down!'

❑ *Exclamatory* sentences make an exclamation and express the emotion of the speaker in the form of an outburst – 'Wow, that's slow!'

These four different forms of sentence are called *moods* in linguistics; there is, therefore, an 'imperative mood', an 'interrogative mood' and so on.

Ways of teaching
As children work on these different types of sentence they will notice certain features about the way the verbs change in the different moods.

About the activities
Photocopiable: Sentence types
In looking at the different types of sentence children may notice the way auxiliaries appear in a number of the interrogative sentences and the way the verb is positioned in the imperative.

Photocopiable: Making different forms of sentence
Using the verbs and nouns available in the tables, children make sentences in different moods. They can make them as absurd as they wish!

Photocopiable: Verb forms
This activity specifically follows the changes in the verbs through sentences that deal with similar subject matter. When children make up their own sentences, they should try to keep the same content but change the mood, noticing the ways in which the verbs change.

Following up
Use of mood: Children can look for different types of sentence around them and see which are most common in certain contexts, such as comics, street signs and so on. When they find an example of a certain type of sentence they can try remodelling the content into a different mood.

Sentence types

There are four types of sentence:

Declarative	Interrogative	Imperative	Exclamatory
States something.	Asks something.	Gives an order.	Exclaims! Sounds surprised! An outburst!
The car is slow.	Is the car slow?	Slow down!	Wow, that's slow!

❑ Sort these sentences into **four** groups by type of sentence.
To make it more difficult all question marks, exclamation marks and full stops have been removed!

Making different forms of sentence

Using the verbs and nouns in the tables below can you make the types of sentence asked for?

You can change the verb from one form to another. Instead of using 'make', you could change it to 'made'.

Verb: make	**Nouns:** sandwich, string	**Sentence type:** declarative

Verb: find	**Nouns:** shoes, table	**Sentence type:** declarative

Verb: eat	**Nouns:** custard, cabbage	**Sentence type:** interrogative

Verb: sniff	**Nouns:** dog, classroom	**Sentence type:** interrogative

Verb: tell	**Nouns:** lemons, home	**Sentence type:** declarative

Verb: shout	**Nouns:** street, sock	**Sentence type:** imperative

Verb forms

❏ Look at this table. It shows a verb in its simple form. Can you change the verb so that it fits into the space in each of the sentences?

Simple verb	Declarative	Interrogative	Imperative
to find	We _____ the lost key.	Can you _____ the lost key?	_____ the lost key.
to tell	Our teacher _____ good jokes.	Does our teacher _____ good jokes?	_____ us a joke.
to eat	Every morning my mum _____ toast for breakfast.	What did your mum _____ for breakfast?	_____ your breakfast.
to go	The car _____ down the street.	Where does the car _____?	_____ down the street.

❏ Now choose **two** of your own verbs. Write sentences for each, changing the verb to fit the different types of sentence.

Declarative

_____

Interrogative

_____

Imperative

_____

Declarative

_____

Interrogative

_____

Imperative

_____

Person

Objective
Identify and experiment with person in verbs

Language issues
Verbs are linked to subjects. A subject is the 'who' or 'what' behind a verb. In 'I swam', the subject is 'I' and the verb is 'swam'. If a command is issued, such as 'Jump' the verb is 'jump' and the subject is whoever the command is addressed to. Subjects and verbs can be in the first, second or third person. The different types of person are indicated by the use of subject pronouns (for example, 'I', 'She') and verbs.

First person verbs identify with the speaker or writer, either alone ('I swam') or as part of a group ('we swam'). Second person verbs identify with one addressed by the speaking or writing ('You must remember...'). Third person verbs identify with a third party or thing who is neither the one addressing nor the one addressed ('He shouted', 'It fell').

Ways of teaching
An understanding of person is essential as children develop the range of writing they produce. Certain texts, such as instructions or postcards, will address the reader directly in the second person ('First you take an egg...', 'Wish you were here...'), whereas other texts will favour other uses of person, such as diaries in the first person or reports of events in the third person.

About the activities
Photocopiable: Person switching
As they switch sentences from one person to another children can look for the different words that change and those that stay the same. When putting a sentence into the third person it is up to them which gender form they use.

Photocopiable: Correct the sentences
Children work through these postcards editing the writing of the Language Bug until it sounds right. Once they have worked on these examples they may want to send examples to one another.

Photocopiable: The rabbit's poem
This is a classic nonsense poem that plays with different persons. Once children have tried to locate the three forms of person requested in the activity they could look for other verbal material, such as the use of the auxiliary verb or the use of singular or plural persons.

Following up
Who is 'she'?: Children can look at a text photocopied or cut out of a newspaper and find the various subject pronouns. They then have to write the type of pronoun identified by these words in the margin or in the space above them.

How would the text change?: Looking at various texts, ask children to work in pairs re-reading them but changing the person. If they are reading a first person text they can put it into third or second person.

Debate: Look at texts that use a third person form for general reference. Education text books are often classic examples, usually referring to the child as 'he' and the teacher as 'she'. Find examples and discuss them with the class. Do they think it is the right way to make general references? Can they think of an alternative?

Person switching

Verbs can be written in the first person, second person or third person.

First person verbs are verbs that point to the writer.
Second person verbs are verbs that point to the reader.
Third person verbs are verbs that point to other things or people.

❑ Rewrite the sentences in the spaces below.
• Change any sentences written in the first person to the second person.
• Change any sentences written in the second person to the third person.
• Change any sentences written in the third person to the first person.

Which verbs changed and which stayed the same? Which other words changed?

I am going to school. ⎯⎯⎯⎯⎯⎯⎯⎯⎯⎯⎯⎯⎯⎯⎯⎯⎯⎯⎯⎯⎯

You play the piano. ⎯⎯⎯⎯⎯⎯⎯⎯⎯⎯⎯⎯⎯⎯⎯⎯⎯⎯⎯⎯⎯⎯

He shouts his name. ⎯⎯⎯⎯⎯⎯⎯⎯⎯⎯⎯⎯⎯⎯⎯⎯⎯⎯⎯⎯⎯⎯

I support United. ⎯⎯⎯⎯⎯⎯⎯⎯⎯⎯⎯⎯⎯⎯⎯⎯⎯⎯⎯⎯⎯⎯⎯⎯

You draw brilliant pictures. ⎯⎯⎯⎯⎯⎯⎯⎯⎯⎯⎯⎯⎯⎯⎯⎯⎯

She says the alphabet quickly. ⎯⎯⎯⎯⎯⎯⎯⎯⎯⎯⎯⎯⎯⎯⎯

You were singing. ⎯⎯⎯⎯⎯⎯⎯⎯⎯⎯⎯⎯⎯⎯⎯⎯⎯⎯⎯⎯⎯⎯⎯

He climbed the rope. ⎯⎯⎯⎯⎯⎯⎯⎯⎯⎯⎯⎯⎯⎯⎯⎯⎯⎯⎯⎯⎯

They play in the park. ⎯⎯⎯⎯⎯⎯⎯⎯⎯⎯⎯⎯⎯⎯⎯⎯⎯⎯⎯⎯

I am all on my own. ⎯⎯⎯⎯⎯⎯⎯⎯⎯⎯⎯⎯⎯⎯⎯⎯⎯⎯⎯⎯⎯⎯

Correct the sentences

❑ Look at the sentences in these letters. Mark the changes that need to be made so that the sentences read correctly. The first one has been done for you.

change

Dear You
Can you ⟨changing⟩ the verbs on this letter so it sound right? Once you has finished reads it back to checking your changes. Remember verbs need to agrees with the rest of the sentence so you is going to have to changes them.
Yours, The Language Bug!

Dear You
You was very clever. I were sure you will not be able to change my last card but you do. Anyway, this one am much harder so see if you makes the right changes this time. Jakes care, there is lots of little traps tucks into the sentences.
Yours, The Language Bug!

Dear You
Curses you be too clever for me. I gives up. It annoy me that you is so good at spot my handiwork. But I will being back another day and will teaches you a lesson. Next time I am win. Me will triumph! Until then sits back and relax because these is my last mistakes. Or is they?
Yours, The Language Bug!

The rabbit's poem

❑ Look at this classic poem and circle or shade over three different types of verb and subject pronoun in three different colours:
- First person verbs and pronouns in green
- Second person verbs and pronouns in blue
- Third person verbs and pronouns in red.

The rabbit's poem

'They told me you had been to her,
And mentioned me to him:
She gave me a good character,
But said I could not swim.

He sent them word I had not gone
(We know it to be true):
If she should push the matter on,
What would become of you?

I gave her one, they gave him two,
You have us three or more;
They all returned from him to you,
Though they were mine before.

If I or she should chance to be
Involved in this affair,
He trusts to you to set them free,
Exactly as we were.

My notion was that you had been
(Before she had this fit)
An obstacle that came between
Him, and ourselves, and it.

Don't let him know she liked them best,
For this must ever be
A secret, kept from all the rest,
Between yourself and me.'

Lewis Carroll

Sentences and readers

Contents of Term 1b

Unit 1:
Audiences and sentences
Review and edit sentences with a view towards the audience of a text

Unit 2:
Standard conventions
Understand some basic conventions of Standard English

Unit 3:
Word order
Investigate word order and key words, looking at the alteration of sentences

Unit 4:
Direct and reported speech
Understand the difference between direct and reported speech

Unit 5:
Reader guides
Understand the ways in which punctuation and the setting out of dialogue aid the reader

This half-term

The units in this half-term look at various factors that feature in the way sentences are presented for readers. These include considerations such as the various methods a writer can use to present speech and the significance of word order. As children undertake these units they should take the opportunity to reflect upon their own writing, particularly of texts that recount events, and consider the way they aim their writing at a reader.

Poster notes

Ways of showing speech
The four most common ways in which texts represent speech are shown on this poster. The two most common ones in narrative text are direct speech and reported speech.

Ways of saying
This is to be used in conjunction with Unit 2. It provides a poster onto which ways of saying particular things can be recorded. The teacher may decide to collect ways of saying 'good', in which case this will be written in the centre. Children can then suggest various standard and non-standard ways of saying something is good, such as 'brill' and 'wicked'. Other 'ways of saying' can be tried, ideas for which can be drawn from the 'Ways of saying' activity.

Ways of showing speech

direct

Sam asked, "What do hedgehogs eat?" Josh replied, "Prickled onions."

Sam asked Josh what hedgehogs ate and Josh told him they ate prickled onions.

reported

scripted

Sam: What do hedgehogs eat?

Josh: Prickled onions.

voice bubbled

Ways of saying

❑ Think of something simple you might want to say, for example, 'That's good', 'I'm ill', 'You're daft!' Think of other ways of saying it, for example, instead of 'That's good' you could say 'That's brill' or 'That's wicked'.

WAYS OF SAYING

Audiences and sentences

Objective
Review and edit sentences with a view towards the audience of a text

Language issues
The audience of an act of communication has a lot of influence upon the way people speak and write. Considerations will include:

❏ the anticipated response of the reader to a text:
Acts of communication are worded in specific ways according to their purpose. Words are selected that match whatever the reader or hearer is expected to do in response to the words. For example, will they persuade them to buy something?

❏ the identity of the reader:
People speak differently to people of different ages or levels of understanding of a subject. The complexity of sentences and vocabulary used will vary depending on who the anticipated audience of a text is.

❏ the relationship between the parties to the communication:
In linguistics this is referred to as the 'tenor' of an act of communication. People will sometimes address their boss in a different way to how they address their friends. The relationship between two people will determine the level of formality used and the tone of the written or spoken exchange.

Ways of teaching
The activities in this unit provide a chance to reflect upon this issue of audience and sentences used in specific contexts. Obviously, children learn a lot about this area in undertaking their own writing activities for a variety of audiences. These activities complement the teaching of this consideration in children's writing, providing examples of language use for discussion.

About the activities
Photocopiable: Sentence types in text types
The activity asks children to separate sentences from two different texts. As they are undertaking the activity the teacher or another child can ask them how they are telling the sentences apart. Observations on how this is done can be collected and shared with the class.

Photocopiable: Scrambling eggs
This recipe is in an absurdly complex style. Once they have finished altering this one children might want to use a thesaurus and try to produce their own complex instructions for simple tasks.

Photocopiable: Formal and informal
Two types of sentence are shown together each saying a similar thing but one written in a more formal style than the other. Once they have grouped the two different sets of sentences, children can revisit the two groups, observing what sort of vocabulary differentiates the two types of communication.

Following up
Relaxed and formal dialogue: As a drama activity children can work in pairs devising either an informal situation into which they inject formal dialogue, or a formal situation that they act out with informal speech. They could create the relaxed interview with the Bank Manager or the very formal meeting of two friends in the park.

Television exchanges: Tape a selection of one-minute exchanges of dialogue from various programmes on the television. Listen to the exchanges and ask the children to discuss the relationship between the participants and how that is reflected in the language. Focus upon two questions: What is the relationship between these people? How does that show in the way they speak to each other? There should be noticeable differences between, for example, a family in a situation comedy, a chat show and an interview on the news.

Card game instructions: Children can read through instructions for various games and try writing their own examples.

Sentence types and text types

❑ Cut out the rectangles.
Some of them belong to the instructions for a game. Some of them belong to a joke.
❑ Collect the sentences from each type of text. Try rebuilding the two texts.

A man was walking down the road and he saw a woman taking a dog for a walk.

And the woman said 'That's true – but this isn't my dog'.

Hold your cards face downwards so that nobody can see them – not even you.

He said 'Hello' and she says 'Hello' back. So he asked 'Does your dog bite?' and the woman said 'No'.

Deal the whole pack of cards between the players.

Take turns to place one card face upwards in the middle of the group.

The man bent over and patted the dog and the dog snapped at him and sunk its teeth into his hand.

The man jumped up and down screaming 'I thought you said your dog doesn't bite'.

To win the game a player must be the first to notice this, place a hand on the cards and shout 'Snap!'

If a card is placed in the pile that bears the same number of pips or picture as the card already in the middle then it is a 'Snap'.

Scrambling eggs

❑ Look at these complicated sentences from an instructional text. Look up any words you don't understand in a dictionary.

❑ Can you alter the sentences to make them easier to understand? Try rewriting the recipe so that someone younger than you could understand it.

Original	Rewrite
To manufacture scrambled eggs:	
Commence by shattering two eggs into a bowl.	
Cudgel the eggs thoroughly by operating a whisk.	
Aggregate a little milk into the mixture.	
Liquefy margarine in a frying pan.	
Gently decant the egg mixture into the pan and stir to scramble.	
Purvey the eggs, on toast if you elect.	

Formal and informal

The rectangles below contain sentences saying similar things.

❑ Can you match one sentence with another, pairing the sentences saying similar things?

❑ Decide which one is more formal and which one is less formal.

I find your behaviour inappropriate.

That telly programme was great.

I enjoyed the television programme immensely.

Please depart.

Would it be possible for me to use the bathroom?

Can I go to the loo?

I don't like the way you're behaving.

Thank you for inviting me to your abode.

Stop doing that.

Thanks for asking me round to your house.

Go away.

I'd love another plate of pudding.

There is an unappealing odour in this room.

The room smells horrible.

I would appreciate it if you would desist.

I would greatly enjoy a further helping of the sweet course.

Standard conventions

Objective
Understand some basic conventions of Standard English

Language issues
Standard English refers to the conventional way in which selected words are combined into sentences. It is a commonly accepted form of communication with a wide audience that understands its vocabulary and conventions. Dialectical forms and words tend to be used and understood within specific regions and, while these make up some of the richest facets of the English language, the conventions of Standard English provide a way of using the language that is most common in public communication. It should be noted that Standard English is, itself, a changing dialect of the language. The ongoing debate about the acceptability of double negatives is an example of the way in which language develops organically.

Ways of teaching
The term 'standard' can be discussed with children and the idea of conventions in the current use of English is presented in this unit. Care must be taken to ensure that no negative value is attached to regional dialects, and the richness they bring to speech and certain types of writing should be emphasized throughout. These activities explore the way the standard form works while also encouraging respect for, and investigation of, diversity.

About the activities
Photocopiable: Broken sentences
This activity explores the way in which sentences are combined in a particular way according to the conventions of grammatical agreement. Children can cut out the sets of half sentences and try arranging the two halves until they sound right.

Photocopiable: Ways of saying
Part of the standardization of English is the way in which certain words and phrases develop an acceptability. By investigating the different ways in which certain things can and have been said in the (not too distant) past children encounter the changes in expression over time.

Photocopiable: Rhyming slang
Through playing with the inventiveness of a particular dialect children can engage with the richness of non-standard dialects. This activity can provide an opportunity to discuss non-standard variations in the language, noticing that the genius of rhyming slang lay in its development as a furtive means of communication in a particular context.

Following up
Talk over time: Children can watch old newsreel footage or children's programmes on video and compare these with current news broadcasting and children's television. They can listen for idiosyncrasies in the language used.

Secret language: Can children devise other ways of communicating in secret with one another? They may already have examples such as passwords and mottoes that they share amongst their inner circle of friends.

Other variations: Following on from the 'Ways of saying' activity children may be able to suggest other actions or descriptions that prompt a range of non-standard terms.

Broken sentences

❑ Match the start of each sentence with its ending.

Every day mum

Every day we

Every day I

catch the bus

catches the bus.

catch the bus.

Tomorrow I

Tomorrow you

Tomorrow she

is going on holiday.

am going on holiday.

are going on holiday.

Yesterday I

Today I

Yesterday my friends

Today my friends

went to the park.

went to the park.

are going to the park.

am going to the park.

My sister said

My brother said

My family said

I said

they wanted a party.

he wanted a party.

I wanted a party.

she wanted a party.

Ways of saying

New ways of expressing things are entering English all the time. During the 1970s young people described something that was good in new ways.

Can you think of some diverse ways in which you and your friends describe the following?

Something is good or brilliant	Feeling ill or sick
Feeling miserable	**Something is bad or just not very good**

Rhyming slang

Rhyming slang is a part of the cockney dialect of East London. It started with speakers using a way of communicating without being understood by people who may have been checking up on them. You may have a similar way of communicating with your friends, using secret words for certain things. It has a brilliant way of working.

1. The start word   2. is rhymed with another word.   3. This rhyming word is now used.

Captain Cook

Sometimes another word linked to the rhyming word is used.

❑ Try inventing your own rhyming slang terms and putting them in a sentence.

Sentence	Explanation
I saw my animal at the pool.	*animal* = creature – rhymes with teacher, *pool* rhymes with school, so 'I saw my teacher at the school'

Word order

Objective
Investigate word order and key words, looking at the alteration of sentences

Language issues
Within a sentence words can be classified as 'content' words or 'function' words. Content words, as their name implies, carry the content of communication. In a sentence like 'The man bit a dog' the two participants ('man', 'dog') and the action ('bit') make up the content of the communication. The two other words are functional. They relate the elements of the sentence content, one with another. Content words can also be called 'open' words. The term 'open' indicates the fact that this category of words is continually being added to as new names are created and new terminology to denote actions is coined. The function category is sometimes described as 'closed', indicating that this category of words tends not to be added to. As sentences are abbreviated into notes or headlines the content words form the crucial element of the abbreviation. With those words it is much easier to recover the meaning of the original text, so a note with 'man bit dog' gives the reader an effective précis of the original sentence.

Ways of teaching
A feel for the difference between these two categories of words will be of use to children developing their note-taking skills. An implicit knowledge of these different types of words also plays a part in the skimming and scanning of texts. As they undertake the activities in this unit they will be asked to look at this basic difference in the two categories of words and to use this understanding in the process of reading and recording information.

About the activities
Photocopiable: Words telling the story
As they focus upon the key words in a newspaper cutting, children need to look for those crucial content words. One way of doing this is to begin by crossing out the words that they think are functional or less important. As they do so, they will begin to isolate the key words carrying the content of the story.

Photocopiable: Recreate the sentence
Once they have altered the sentences children can compare their revisions and look at some of the common

changes made. Certain word types are commonly moved or a sentence is taken from a passive or active voice into the alternative voice.

Photocopiable: Words that count
This activity involves children working in pairs trying to read the content of two passages with access to different types of words. Firstly they look at text (a), which will probably help very little. However they could suggest what could feature around the words on text (a). Next they hand text (a) back in and receive text (b). This is much easier to reconstruct. Having completed this they can look at the two texts together and try to read the passage.

Following up
Headlines: Reading items clipped out of the newspaper without their headlines, children can devise suitable headlines for news stories. If children work on the same story they can compare their headlines and see if they had any words in common.

Story from headline: Looking at headlines cut from a newspaper ask children if they can guess what the content of the story may have been. Ask them to make some brief notes on this before giving them a copy of the actual story to read.

Note-taking: Record a news item from the radio news and play it to a group of children, asking them to make notes as they listen. Once they have done this they can try retelling the story, working round the group, contributing a fact or detail at a time. When this is complete they can listen to the original and see how close they came to recounting all the details.

Words telling the story

❑ Look at **five** newspaper stories and complete the grid. For each story record:

The headline	A note explaining the story	Ten words crucial to the story

Recreate the sentence

❑ Look at the sentences in the boxes on the left. Try to reword each of these sentences so that they say the same thing but in a different way.

Original	New version
On Tuesday we are going to the library.	
My friend kicked the ball and accidentally broke the window.	
My friend let me use his bike to ride to school today.	
Tomorrow late children will stay in for the whole of playtime.	
After dinner we went to science club instead of going out to play.	
My little brother crawled into the garden and we found him eating a worm from the flower bed.	
There is an odd smell coming from the cellar and we have to hold our noses when we go past.	
I don't like custard but I like every other pudding.	
The green apples were bruised because they fell out of the basket.	
We went to the park then we had our tea.	

Which words did you change? How did you change the order of the words?

Words that count

❑ Fill in the spaces so that the sentences make sense.

(Invention a)

The _____ _____ was _____ in _____. _____ of _____ was _____ around _____ _____. He _____ the _____ _____ _____. In his _____ _____ _____ _____ of _____ _____ out of a _____. These _____ _____ a _____. It was _____ as a _____.

(Invention b)

_____ steam engine _____ invented _____ Africa. Hero _____ Alexandria _____ born _____ 20CE. _____ invented _____ first steam engine. _____ _____ simple machine two jets _____ steam spurted _____ _____ _____ container. _____ jets turned _____ sphere. _____ _____ used _____ _____ toy.

(Body a)

_____ are _____ by _____ _____ the _____ of our _____. When the _____ _____ it can _____ the _____ _____ under the _____. They _____ _____ and this _____ up as a _____ _____. This is a _____. The _____ is _____ up of _____ _____ from _____ _____ and _____. If the _____ is _____ the _____ can _____ up to _____ a _____.

(Body b)

Bruises _____ made _____ objects hitting _____ flesh _____ _____ bodies. _____ _____ object hits _____ _____ damage _____ blood vessels _____ _____ skin. _____ release blood _____ _____ shows _____ _____ _____ purple patch. _____ _____ _____ bruise. _____ bruise _____ made _____ _____ fluid released _____ blood vessels _____ cells. _____ _____ head _____ struck _____ bruise _____ swell _____ _____ make _____ bump.

Direct and reported speech

Objective
Understand the difference between direct and reported speech

Language issues
The words of others can be represented in various ways in writing. This can range from a transcript, recording the speech verbatim, to a summary of what someone said in a speech. The lengthiest of speeches can be condensed into a one sentence summary.

One significant difference is between the direct quotation of speech with the corresponding use of speech marks and the reporting of speech in a way that gives the idea or gist of what was said but does not quote the actual words. So we can directly quote someone: *Victoria said "We are not amused."* Or indirectly report it: *Victoria said she was not amused.* Reporting can involve an element of summing up what was said: *Victoria expressed displeasure.*

Ways of teaching
The crucial difference between direct and reported speech lies in whether or not the words on the page are presented as a quotation of what was said. Work on this

unit should provide an opportunity to revise work on speech marks and the way in which they guide readers, as well as investigating these two ways of presenting what was said.

About the activities
Photocopiable: Direct and reported
Looking at the two sets of rectangles children can try to match direct with reported representations of the same pieces of speech. Some of the speech acts are remarkably similar so children will need to check carefully to ensure that they have matched the right rectangles together.

Photocopiable: Who said what?
Through completing the voice bubbles children will be turning reported speech into the words that could have been said. They can use their own judgement on the exact wording. When the text says 'I agreed' the narrator could have a voice bubble containing the words 'I agree' or 'You're right' – or even plain 'Yeah!'

Photocopiable: Change the style
As with the above activity children may need to use creative judgement to decide what actual words might have been used in producing the speech acts reported.

Following up
Finding: Children can look through different types of text that contain speech in order to find which contain reported and direct speech. Interesting examples could include history books that narrate the events of a particular time, modern novels and different levels of a reading scheme.

Comic contexts: Taking the conversation that takes place in a comic story as their starting point children can look at how much of a comic story is dependent upon the pictures. They can try recording the dialogue from some of the pictures separately and see how much sense it makes standing alone. They could then look in the comic story and see what the context of the picture contributed to the speech.

Plays and pictures: Using a scripted text such as a playscript children can try turning this format into a comic story. They will need to account for who said what to whom, and should draw the characters with their speech bubbles.

Direct and reported

Speech can be presented

directly, as direct quotation
in speech marks
giving the words that were said, eg:

> *Mum said, "Take those muddy
> boots off."*
> *I said, "It's not fair."*

indirectly, as reported speech
not in speech marks
stating what was said, eg:

> *Mum told us to take our
> muddy boots off.*
> *I said it wasn't fair.*

❑ Look at the rectangles below. Sort the rectangles containing direct speech from rectangles containing reported speech. Try matching direct rectangles with the reported rectangles which report the same speech.

I pleaded with the dragon not to eat me.	The teacher told the children not to whisper in assembly.	Our teacher said "Open that window."
I called to Jack to throw the ball to me.		Our teacher asked us to open a particular window.
I pleaded "Please don't eat me" with the dragon.	Mum asked where the hammer was.	Our teacher said we could open any window.
Our teacher said "Open any window you like."	"Don't whisper in assembly," the teacher told the children.	"Jack," I shouted, "Throw the ball to me."
Mum asked "Where's the hammer?"	The dragon said it had plans to eat me.	The dragon said "I plan to eat you."

Who said what?

❑ Look at the comic story. The bubbles are blank. Can you fill in the bubbles with your suggestions as to what each character might have said?

Our teacher said it was raining so we had to stay inside. We all moaned about how much we hated staying in.

We got all the games out. Lisa pointed out most of them were broken. I agreed.

Just then Saleh looked out the window and said the sun was coming out. We all cheered.

We all went to the window. It was still raining. Saleh said he had been joking. We told him it wasn't funny.

Change the style

❑ Look at the left hand column. Rewrite the sentences in the right hand column. Change reported speech to direct speech and direct speech to reported speech.

Original text	Rewritten text
Mum said she was making chips for tea so I told her they were my favourites.	
I asked, "Can we go swimming?" "The pool is closed today", Dad replied.	
The cyclist warned everyone to get out of the way because his brakes were not working.	
The teacher said, "Sit down and answer your names on the register," then he added, "Where is the register?"	
I asked if I could type my story on the computer and my teacher agreed.	
"I'll be ninety on Saturday," my gran whispered. "She's doing a parachute jump to celebrate," my mum added.	
My friend, Amy, told us she was moving house and we said we didn't want her to go.	
"I'm cold," the boy said. "Well run up and down the stairs to warm up a bit," his mum responded.	
Reuben told the life guard he had seen a boat in trouble so the life guard said he would see for himself.	
"Get out of my garden," the next door neighbour barked, but the dog just said "Woof woof!"	

Reader guides

Objective

To understand the ways in which punctuation and the setting out of dialogue aid the reader

Language issues

In spoken language there are all sorts of stresses and pauses a speaker can use in order to assist the listener's understanding. One example of this is the slight pitch change people make just after saying 'So I said...' to indicate that the words that follow are the actual words said on a previous occasion now quoted. In written English this is done through a variety of means. Punctuation marks can indicate the barriers between what is and is not quoted very effectively, as well as the items in a list and the completion of a sentence.

Ways of teaching

As children develop an appreciation of the role performed by punctuation their ability to use it in writing is enhanced. They know why a particular mark is useful so they use it. In this unit children should begin to discuss the usefulness of particular punctuation points and the role they play in assisting the reader.

About the activities

Photocopiable: Helping the reader

This tightly written piece of dialogue is one example of Philip Ridley's excellent presentation of speech in his novels. Children should locate speech marks, commas, capital letters, exclamation marks, question marks, an ellipsis (three dots showing pauses) and full stops. Can they analyse the role some of these marks are playing in assisting the reading of the passage?

Photocopiable: Unhelpful sentences

The puzzling read these sentences present is an important part of the exercise. By working out what is being said, children can also investigate the ways in which punctuation would ordinarily help them to read the sentences.

Photocopiable: Pick an argument

Children need to work on this in groups of six or less. They cut out the slips of paper and these are placed face downwards in the middle of the group. The teacher gives a set time, around ten minutes, for them to write one of the arguments shown on the slips using lots of speech, clearly demarcated. Once this is clear everyone picks a slip and has to start writing. After ten minutes everyone

changes their slips around and tries to do the same with the new argument.

Following up

Punctuation history: If children have access to pieces of writing they did in the past, either from record folders or by bringing samples in from home, they can trace their own punctuation history. This involves looking at how they learned to use certain marks at certain times and how this has improved their writing.

Particular punctuation!: This unit provides an opportunity for children to review the punctuation points that they use with confidence and those that they still need to learn. They can decide which ones they plan to perfect over the coming half-term.

Page scanning: Children can try to scan pages of text briefly and then to recall what punctuation marks they saw on the page to a friend, who then checks their recollection by looking at the text.

Helping the reader

❏ Look at this passage from 'Kaspar and the Glitter'. It is the scene in which Kaspar has entered the city called 'The Gloom' and has met Jingo. Find the different pieces of layout and punctuation that help the reader. Note these down in the margins.

'This way, if you please, Master Kasper,' said Jingo.
He led Kasper into a long and gloomy alleyway.

Their footsteps echoed all round them.

Now that Jingo didn't have the basket to carry, he wasn't quite sure what to do with his hands. To keep them occupied, he picked up his dirty jacket tails, muttered, 'Gracious me!' then brushed them clean. When they were clean, he let them fall back to the ground, whereupon they soon got dirty again, so he picked them up once more, muttered another 'Gracious me!' and brushed them all over again.

Kasper watched Jingo in amazement for a while, then looked round the alleyway.

The City doesn't look very sparkling, thought Kasper. All I can see at the moment are leaking drainpipes, broken windows and piles of rubbish. And this alleyway smells revolting. It needs a good dose of bleach and disinfectant.

'And now, Master Kasper,' began Jingo, his voice bubbling with excitement, 'it's my turn to surprise you.'

'It is?' said Kasper.

'Have you any idea who I'm going to cook the pie for?'

'None at all.'

'Master Kasper,' he said 'you are holding the ingredients that will make the favourite pie of ...' And here he took a deep breath so he could say it loudly and with pride, 'The King.'

'The King?' said Kasper. 'The King of what?'

'The King of The Gloom, of course,' Jingo replied. 'KING STREETWISE!'

And his voice echoed up and down the alley.

'STREETWISE ... TREETWISE ... REETWISE ... EETWISE ... TWISE ... WISE ... ISE ... SSSSS.'

Kasper and the Glitter
Philip Ridley

Unhelpful sentences

❏ Look at these sentences. They are difficult to read. Can you rewrite them using punctuation to make them more readable?

mum said its very cold I quite agree said gran

our teacher said playtime great said shaun lets get the football

the cows said moo good morning the farmer shouted

the clock says eight o clock said my mum I'd better be going

my gran said she was feeling fit give you a race I said O.K. she replied

put your coat on mum said why I moaned because I say so she said

the forecast said it could rain joe said I hope it doesn't I replied

lisa said she was bored and danny said lets go out on bikes

_____

_____

_____

_____

_____

_____

_____

Pick an argument

❑ Cut out these strips and pick an argument!

Two people arguing over which one of them was the first to get to the supermarket checkout.

A mum arguing with her child who is being really stroppy in a cafe.

A hare arguing with a tortoise about which one of them would win a race.

A driving instructor telling his or her pupil off for driving so badly and the pupil disagreeing.

A kettle arguing with a saucepan about which of them is the most useful.

A dog arguing with its owner that the walk they just went on was too short.

Nouns and pronouns

Contents of Term 2a

This half-term

Following on from the revision of nouns, this half-term focuses upon pronouns. The main elements of this focus are a look at the way in which pronouns stand in for nouns, and the effects this can have on the clarity of a sentence.

Poster notes

Types of nouns
This poster provides a brief summation of the qualities of a noun and supports the revision activities in Unit 1. As children revisit the function of nouns the poster provides a way of identifying them within sentences.

Pronouns
The poster links with Unit 2 and provides a reference point showing the various types of pronoun. As children work on pronouns it provides a useful resource to refer to, defining the different jobs that pronouns can do. The classification of pronouns is a complex activity but this poster can provide an insight into the wide range of words that are included in this word class.

Types of nouns

❏ A noun is a word for a thing. It could be a thing you see.

It could be a thing you feel.

It could be an abstract thing you just know.

If you can imagine saying 'a', 'an' or 'the' before a word – then it is a noun.

Pronouns

demonstrative

points to a particular noun mentioned in the text,
eg, *this* in *This is my house.*

interrogative

used in questions,
eg, *who* in *Who is having tea?*

indefinite

refers to someone or something without knowing its name,
eg, *something* in *Something made a noise.*

personal

indicates a person,
eg, *she* in *She plays football.*

reflexive

refers to someone or something already mentioned in the sentence,
eg, *herself* in *She made tea for herself.*

relative

links one part of a sentence to another,
eg, *who* in *Joe is a boy who likes singing.*

reciprocal

covers two people or things that are together,
eg, *one another* in *The girls waved to one another.*

Noun sorts

Objective
Revisit the different types of nouns

Language issues
Nouns are words that name things or feelings. This class of words includes all words that can act as subjects in a sentence, so if a word can follow the articles 'a', 'an' or 'the' in a sentence then it is a noun. This means that words like 'walk', which would commonly be classed as a verb, can be classed as a noun in a sentence like 'We are going for a walk'. The verb here is 'going', because that is the action 'we' are taking. Nouns can often be detected by the way they can be turned from singular to plural and vice versa. In this example 'We' could go for a number of 'walks': 'We are going for a few walks'. Although the plurals made may seem odd the pluralization rule acts as another useful test of a noun.

Ways of teaching
The ability to say 'a', 'an' and 'the' before a word, along with the pluralization test, provide two ways of identifying nouns. In this unit children investigate the process of identifying nouns and revisit some of the different types of nouns.

About the activities
Photocopiable: Is this a noun?
In applying the 'a', 'an' or 'the' test children can be asked to think of a context in which a construction can work. It is difficult to think of an example in which we

would say 'a soft' but we can imagine talking about 'a jump' in a context like 'She did a brilliant jump'. This helps us to determine which of these two words could be used as a noun.

Photocopiable: Finding nouns
As children swap the nouns around in this activity they will need to check that the sentences they make include consistent uses of single and plural nouns.

Photocopiable: Nounsearch
As they undertake this activity children will need to be reminded of the various types of nouns (see poster).

Following up
Headlines: Children can look at the headlines of newspaper stories and find words that are used as verbs in the headlines but could be used as nouns in a different sentence, for example, 'Talks crumble in Union row'. They can cut them out and create the new sentence around them.

Dictionary nouns: Taking any page in the dictionary, children can go through the words listed testing them to see if they could be used as nouns.

Jumble sentences: Taking several sentences from a story, children can try jumbling the nouns around to make a nonsensical opening.

Is this a noun?

A noun is a word for a thing.

It could be a thing you see.

It could be a thing you feel.

It could be an abstract thing you just know.

If you can imagine saying 'a', 'an' or 'the' before a word – then it is a noun.

❑ Sort these words into **two** separate lists:
- words we could use as nouns
- words we don't use as nouns.

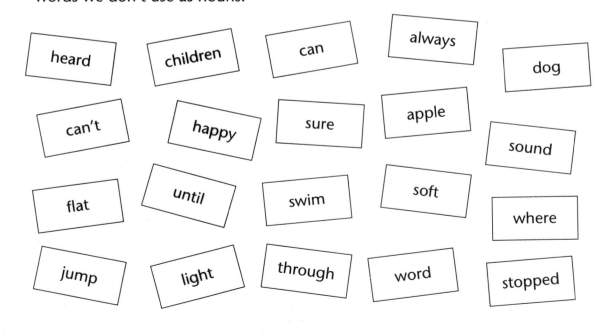

heard children can always dog

can't happy sure apple sound

flat until swim soft where

jump light through word stopped

Scholastic Literacy Skills
Grammar and punctuation

Finding nouns

❑ Cut out the nouns from these sentences and swap them round to make new sentences.
For example:

Please pass the sugar

and

Don't feed the tiger

Please pass the	tiger

Could be cut
and pasted into:

Don't feed the	sugar

✂

Please pass the sugar.

The pencils need sharpening.

Can I eat a biscuit?

Don't feed the tiger.

The rain is heavy, use this umbrella.

Quick! Pass me the fire extinguisher.

Could I borrow your handkerchief?

You can throw those sweet wrappers in the bin.

We ate fish and chips for tea.

I put your dirty socks and pants in the laundry basket.

Nounsearch

❏ Look in the grid to find the following
- five singular concrete nouns
- five plural concrete nouns.
- five abstract nouns

d	a	h	e	j	s	c	l	o	t	h	e	s	j	l	v
o	b	c	l	k	h	c	l	d	g	d	b	u	l	k	c
g	j	a	h	s	i	v	b	a	l	l	o	o	n	g	l
f	s	p	r	i	r	j	q	o	l	w	g	o	o	t	d
s	h	a	t	u	t	r	p	p	r	u	p	p	s	k	t
a	e	e	e	p	d	d	g	h	u	d	h	d	a	e	s
d	e	g	m	i	f	i	r	s	w	h	a	g	p	w	i
n	t	h	i	g	k	l	g	e	b	b	p	j	u	m	p
e	q	j	s	w	o	r	r	y	n	c	p	b	a	b	y
s	a	d	e	f	e	y	r	t	m	s	i	r	m	h	e
s	t	s	r	j	r	i	e	y	x	a	n	d	y	k	a
y	i	u	y	w	s	e	p	b	s	l	e	a	o	l	h
o	x	i	b	i	r	t	h	d	a	y	s	n	k	g	t
e	n	j	o	y	m	e	n	t	r	m	s	x	s	s	s

dog	dogs	happiness
balloon	birthdays	misery
baby	enjoyment	jump
books	worry	shirt
clothes	sadness	sheet

The function of pronouns

Objective
Revise the function of pronouns

Language issues
Pronouns are words that act as substitutes for nouns. If, instead of saying, 'Jack ate breakfast' we substitute 'it' for the noun 'breakfast' we make the new sentence 'Jack ate it'. There are different functions pronouns can perform:

❑ *demonstrative*: this is when pronouns point out a specific thing, such as 'this', 'that'.

❑ *interrogative:* these are pronouns that raise a question, such as 'which' and 'what'. They refer to the noun that forms the answer to the question. For example, in the question 'What is London?' the pronoun 'What' stands in for the noun 'A city'.

❑ *indefinite:* a pronoun can be used to stand for the person or quantity not yet identified such as 'anyone' or 'something'.

❑ *personal:* pronouns that refer to people such as 'she', 'we' and 'they'.

❑ *reflexive:* pronouns ending in a form of the ending '-self', such as 'himself' and 'ourselves'.

❑ *relative:* linking information about a noun to the noun, such as 'who' in 'the man who lives here', and 'that' in 'the dog that dug a hole'.

❑ *reciprocal:* used to cover parties relating to one another, such as 'each other'. In the sentence 'Jack and Jill blamed one another' the reciprocal pronoun 'one another' stands in for 'Jack and Jill'.

Ways of teaching
The categories of pronoun are complex and the emphasis of this unit is not upon children learning each of them. Instead the unit encourages children to reflect upon the fact that there are different ways in which pronouns can take the place of nouns.

About the activities
Photocopiable: Find the pronouns
As a revision of pronouns, this activity involves locating them in sentences. One way into this activity is for children to delete words they are sure are *not* pronouns.

Photocopiable: Types of pronoun
After looking at the definitions of pronouns children are asked to locate examples for each one. There are two examples for each definition, but it is up to the teacher whether or not to tell that to the class.

Photocopiable: The door
This story plays with pronouns. Children are asked to locate examples of different types of pronoun in the story.

Following up
Pop pronouns: Children can guess which type of pronoun is the most common and then participate in a tallying activity, reading texts and charting how often a particular type of pronoun appears.

Extend the examples: Ask the children to try and find more examples of the different types of pronoun other than those given in the unit.

Find the pronouns

❏ Find the pronouns in these sentences and circle them.
Are they referring to things or people and are they asking questions?

This is my house.

That is the fire escape.

What is the capital city of Egypt?

Where is the light switch?

Does anyone want a cup of tea?

Someone tidied up.

She is playing football.

We are going there after school.

I can cook for myself.

My mum treated herself to this bar of chocolate.

Can you stop arguing with each other?

This is the book that I lost yesterday.

Types of pronoun

There are nine different types of pronoun – demonstrative, interrogative, indefinite, personal, reflexive, relative and reciprocal.

❏ For each sentence circle the pronoun and identify the pronoun type.

These are my hands.	
What is your name?	
Which coat is yours?	
Yuuk – something smells bad!	
They are eating cakes.	
That was a good game.	
Share your ideas with one another.	
The boy hurt himself on the climbing frame.	
We are hungry.	
Sam is the boy whose mum flies aeroplanes.	
The children helped each other make dinner.	
Somebody made a mess.	
You can help yourself to sandwiches.	
Mavis is a goat who can sing.	

The door

❏ Look at the text below. Find the pronouns and circle them. Write the type of pronoun they are above the circle.

The story with a creepy house

They approached the house which stood, deserted,

beyond the trees. They were all scared but she persuaded

them to walk right up to that open door she had seen

from the road. She pushed the door open.

'Where are you going?' somebody asked.

'I have come this far,' she replied 'I am not going back.'

Someone said 'We won't go in there.'

'Suit yourself,' she said, too late.

They had run away.

She stepped inside, reassuring herself by saying aloud, 'I

don't need them. I can look after myself,'

as slowly, the door creaked shut behind her.

Noun and pronoun play

Objective
Investigate the function of pronouns and their reference

Language issues
Pronouns can be odd words to use. They are confusing without a clear idea of who or what they are referring to. This is a feature that can be used to full effect in advertising slogans such as 'You know it makes sense'. The slogan is memorable but vague enough to make us wonder what the pithy little sentence referred to. The vagueness and ambiguity of pronouns are also at the root of humorous exchanges such as the style of joke used many times in the film *Airplane*:

Pilot: Hostess, take this to the cockpit!
Hostess: What is it?
Pilot: It's a little room at the front of the plane with controls and things, but that's not important right now.

Ways of teaching
This unit allows a bit of enjoyment of the ambiguity of pronouns. The examples included show various levels of playing with pronouns and trying to decipher what they refer to.

About the activities
Photocopiable: Pronoun tales
Once they have tried the examples on this photocopiable page, children could try to produce their own examples. Challenge them to tell a story that uses pronouns frequently but that the hearers can understand, such as those on the photocopiable page.

Photocopiable: Knots
If children take an interest in *Knots* (Penguin Books, 1970, ISBN 0-14-003350-5) in this activity it may be worth showing them some others selected from the book. Some are very complex but there are a few innovative and entertaining ones that children can enjoy.

Photocopiable: Catch the pronoun
Make sure children work in twos on this and encourage them to act out the script, pointing as they go. When they encounter a pronoun they can point towards the person or thing it refers to.

Following up
Retell stories: Children can try retelling well known stories as pronoun tales, seeing how reductive their result can be and if anyone can recognize the original story from the end result. For example:

They went out. She came in. Didn't eat his. Didn't eat hers but did eat his. Didn't sit on his, didn't sit on hers but did sit on his.

Do you recognize *Goldilocks and the three bears*?

Something Else: Something Else by Kathleen Cave (Picture Puffins, 1995, ISBN 0-14-054907-2) is a picture book in which the characters' names are made up of pronouns. It proves to be an excellent story about how an 'I' accepts a 'You', making a 'They' friendship.

Script pointing: Look in other scripts to see how items and people in the text are referred to using pronouns and how this may lead the actor to point or use other gestures to indicate who is being referred to.

Pronoun tales

❑ Look at these stories and try to work out what events could have happened in each of them. For example, you might want to ask the following questions: Who is 'he'? Where is 'there'?

He said goodbye to her. She went there and he went elsewhere. He bought these for her. He went there to meet her. He saw her. He hid them. She saw him but didn't see them. They went there and he gave these to her. She thanked him.

I went there. They were not there. I played then they came. He said I couldn't play there but they said I could. They told him I could. He went away. They let me stay. We played together. He hid from them. He went there. They were there but they didn't see him. He found those. He put those in this and jumped out of there. He came back to here with these. They saw these were not there but they don't know these are here.

❑ Can you write an explanation for one of the stories?

Knots

In 1969 RD Laing published a book of poems about the way people relate to other people and things. He called the poems *Knots*. Here are two of them.

They are playing a game. They are playing at not
playing a game. If I show them I see they are, I
shall break the rules and they will punish me.
I must play their game, of not seeing I see the game.

RD Laing

I want it
I get it
therefore I am good

I want it
I don't get it
therefore I am bad

I am bad
    because I didn't get it

I am bad
    because I wanted what I didn't get

I must take care
    to get what I want
    and want what I get
    and not get what I don't want

RD Laing

❑ Look at the poems. What do you think they are about? How do they cleverly use pronouns? Could you write a poem using pronouns in a similar way?

Catch the pronoun

❑ Read this script with a partner then look through it finding the different pronouns. Circle them and make a note in the right margin of what, or who, the pronouns refer to. The first example is done for you.

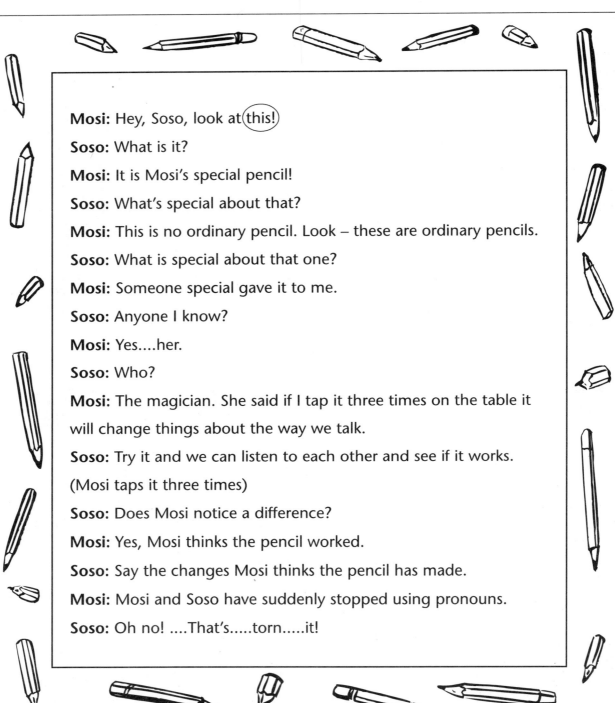

Mosi: Hey, Soso, look at (this!)   – the penc

Soso: What is it?

Mosi: It is Mosi's special pencil!

Soso: What's special about that?

Mosi: This is no ordinary pencil. Look – these are ordinary pencils.

Soso: What is special about that one?

Mosi: Someone special gave it to me.

Soso: Anyone I know?

Mosi: Yes....her.

Soso: Who?

Mosi: The magician. She said if I tap it three times on the table it will change things about the way we talk.

Soso: Try it and we can listen to each other and see if it works.

(Mosi taps it three times)

Soso: Does Mosi notice a difference?

Mosi: Yes, Mosi thinks the pencil worked.

Soso: Say the changes Mosi thinks the pencil has made.

Mosi: Mosi and Soso have suddenly stopped using pronouns.

Soso: Oh no! ....That's.....torn.....it!

Making sense

Objective
Understand, check and redraft sentences, looking at agreement of nouns, pronouns and verbs

Language issues
Agreement involves the consistent use of words combined with other words. In sentences, nouns and pronouns agree with the verbs with which they form a clause. For example, the verb 'to be' changes according to whether the subject of the verb is singular or plural. The noun 'Ali' is followed by the verb 'is' (as in 'Ali is six'), whereas the noun 'rabbits' is followed by 'are' (as in 'Rabbits are fast').

Ways of teaching
For children developing their grasp of the language, agreement can be a big issue. It can sometimes show in inconsistencies in the written work of children who are struggling to express themselves. The emphasis in this unit is upon children investigating the way in which we use agreement in speech. For competent language users this is second nature. The teacher needs to bear in mind that inconsistencies may occur due to conventions of dialect (as in 'We was robbed'). As with all such variations there is something there to note and investigate as another example of a rich and diverse language.

About the activities
Photocopiable: Sounds O.K.
Much of the understanding that competent language users have of this subject of agreement is, in fact, implicit. Sentences just 'sound right' or 'sound odd'. This activity explores that, asking children to say certain sentences and remodel them so they sound right. One interesting feature of this activity is the fact that, to a certain extent, the participant has to understand the odd sentence to be able to remodel it!

Photocopiable: Join the sentence
This activity is like a jigsaw. Some of the strips on the left will fit several of the strips on the right, those containing the second halves of sentences. So, children need to look

at all the strips and try them out before creating a full set of sentences that demonstrate agreement.

Photocopiable: Right space, right pronoun
As with 'Join the sentence' the full set of sentences needs to be worked on in one go. Some sentences may be repaired in a number of ways but the key to the activity is to find a set of sentences that all agree.

Following up
Create own oddities: Children can try to create their own oddities, looking at what they need to do to create sentences like the ones in 'Sounds O.K.' If they have a grasp of the idea of agreement they will be able to see which words they can change in a sentence to create such oddities.

Swapping pronouns in a text: Looking at a paragraph from a novel, children can try changing every pronoun with the aim of creating a new paragraph that reads consistently.

Circle the agreeables: Children can write sentences on the whiteboard and try circling words that have to agree with other words and linking them.

Sounds O.K.

❑ Look at the sentences in the boxes below. Each of them needs to be changed to make sense. Write the changed version in the box alongside.

He play in the park.	
They was finishing their dinner.	
I is tying my laces.	
You am going to be late.	
Zoe are tidying the bookcase.	
Rashid and Lara is playing cards together.	
We is going out to play.	
He found him pencil on the floor.	
I saw they on the bus.	
Jack were finishing his work.	

Join the sentence

❑ Match the slips on the left hand side of the page with slips on the right hand side of the page to make a set of **ten** sentences that make sense.

The marbles fell out of the bag and

it is sunny.

Our dog ran into the house and

they rolled under the table.

I called for my friend and

she was not at home.

My sister came home and

gave it to my teacher.

I called for my friend but

it was raining.

I collected my books and

I made her a drink.

I found my maths book and

he rolled under the table.

You can come to my house and

gave them to the librarian.

We wanted to play outside but

we will play computer games.

We are going out to play and

we went to the cinema.

Right space, right pronoun

❑ The pronouns in these sentences are mixed up. Can you cut them out and rearrange them to make sense?

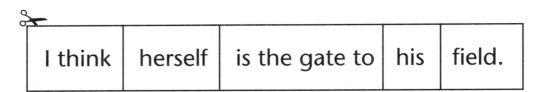

| I think | herself | is the gate to | his | field. |

| I wonder | someone | is the name of | she | street? |

| Listen, | himself | is coming. |

| Mum said | this | wanted to be all by | what. |

| My little brother can tie | that | shoe laces by | this. |

Clarity

Objective
Ensure clear reference in using pronouns

Language issues
Pronouns can be ambiguous, as was noted in Unit 3. This is because they are used to refer to other things that the reader should be able to identify. The name Abraham Lincoln denotes a specific, historical character. The words 'this' and 'he' could refer to any number of nouns. In themselves they have no particular identity. If they are used in the sentence 'This is Abraham Lincoln' or 'He was Abraham Lincoln' these two pronouns develop a particular meaning. In short, the meanings of pronouns derive from their context.

Pronouns can refer forward or backwards. A forward reference occurs when they refer to something that has yet to be identified in the text, such as 'This is Abraham Lincoln', in which the 'this' precedes the specific noun. This is called *cataphoric* reference. If the pronoun follows the specific noun to which it refers, as in 'My house is this one', this is called *anaphoric* reference. In both these cases the pronoun refers to a noun placed elsewhere in a text that needs to be understood for it to make sense.

Ways of teaching
In this unit children investigate examples of clear and unclear reference in pronouns. Through experiencing both they can build up an understanding of this issue which they can then apply in their own use of English.

About the activities
Photocopiable: Who is who?
As they explore the reference of various pronouns children will find some interesting examples in this passage. There are pronouns that refer to the reader and pronouns that denote the narrator ('I...'). One subject this passage raises for discussion is how we know certain people are referred to by the specific pronouns.

Photocopiable: Pronouns in use
Through exploring the use of pronouns in other texts children can develop an understanding of uses of these words in real contexts.

Photocopiable: Two ways of reading it
The ambiguity of pronouns can result in some interesting sentences. In these examples there are two ways of reading each sentence and, while there may be an obvious reading it is tempting to explore the alternative.

Following up
Double meaning: Children can try to devise their own sentences that have the potential for two meanings. It may help if they look at the examples in 'Two ways of reading it' and then try to use the same pronouns.

Cinema posters: Look at video trailers and adverts for films in the newspaper. These often use pronouns as a way of enticing potential viewers. A whole generation of fans of the film *ET* was drawn by the pronominal 'He's afraid, he's alone, he's a million miles from home'. Slogan's like 'He's back' and 'Just when you thought it was safe' are deliberately open and ambiguous. Children can try devising their own trailer slogans for stories they know.

Redrafting: Children can look back through their own writing and consider their own use of pronouns. They could use the 'Pronouns in use' chart to record some of their usages and look to see how clearly they used them.

Who is who?

❏ Circle the pronouns in this passage from Andrew Gibson's 'The Great Querne' (from the book *The Rollickers*). Can you point out who or what each pronoun refers to?

There were four of them: Thornton, Ern, Roxella and the Duchess. They were all children; all of them were unusual; and I shall not try to tell you how they got their names – or rather, if I remember rightly, nicknames. They were all sitting in a small room, hugging their knees, and looking very miserable.

'I had not realized,' said the Duchess, pulling thoughtfully at one of her many red curls, 'that life could be so flat'.

'Nor me, Duchess' said Thornton, 'nor me'.

Thornton and the Duchess spoke in a rather peculiar way, and you may as well get used to it now.

'Whose fault is it, Thornton?' the Duchess asked. She had something of a soft spot for him, ...

Pronouns in use

❑ Collect some texts together, including some stories. Find **ten** sentences that contain pronouns and complete the grid below. Record the pronouns, the sentence in which you found them and the people or things to which the sentence refers.

Pronoun	Sentence it appears in	Who or what referred to

Two ways of reading it

❑ Look at these sentences. Each of them could be read in two ways. In the first one the pronoun 'He' could refer to the dog – or Harry! Try finding the possible double meanings for each of the other sentences.

My friend Harry has got a dog. He is smelly.

Harry smells.   The dog smells.

Our school had a bike shed but it got knocked down.

_____   _____

The teachers played football against the children and they lost.

_____   _____

My brother and sister found some broken toys so we put them in the bin.

_____   _____

Our teacher has got a gerbil. We like watching him run round in his wheel.

_____   _____

I looked in the car for my glove but found it in the washing machine.

_____   _____

My sisters fed the rabbits. They have floppy ears and funny teeth.

_____   _____

Long and short sentences

Contents of Term 2b

This half-term

The reworking of sentences and punctuating of longer sentences forms the main focus of this half-term. As children develop their use of grammar they develop the ability to create longer and more complex sentences. Some units look at some of the choices writers make as they create the sentences they desire.

Poster notes

Connectives
The poster lists various words and phrases that can act as connectives. These words play a vital role in the construction of longer and more complex sentences. The poster will be of particular use in Unit 2 and is supported by the poster in the Term 3a section of this book.

Punctuation marks
The list of punctuation marks provides a resource to be used in identifying the various ways sentences can be demarcated. It can be used in looking out for the various punctuation marks and seeing what jobs they do. A copy could be made and examples of uses of the various marks recorded alongside.

Connectives

also

but

additionally

later

furthermore

nevertheless

however

earlier

so that

just then

because

after

therefore

then

and

Punctuation marks

Hyphen

?
Question mark

Full stop

A
Capital letter

,
Comma

!
Exclamation mark

" "
Speech marks

Colon

,
Semicolon

'
Apostrophe

Dash

Contracting sentences

Objective

Explore telegraphic sentences and their ambiguities

Language issues

Contractions of sentences can be used for note-taking purposes, to create headlines or to summarize story contents in a blurb. In such cases the context of the contracted form or the understanding of the reader should enable the meaning of the sentence to become clear. Such sentences do, however, leave themselves open to ambiguity. When sentences are contracted there is a need for a balance between a decrease in the number of words and the need for the original meaning still to be recoverable.

Ways of teaching

The examples given in this activity of potential ambiguities are quite extreme ones. However the awareness of a writer that a reader could read a text in a misleading way is an important part of writing. A sentence like 'The boy told the man he was old' is open to two readings in which the boy could be referring either to himself or the man as 'old'. As children develop their writing skills in Key Stage 2 there is this crucial awareness of the needs of the audience and the support the writer can offer them that underpins an avoidance of such potential ambiguities.

About the activities

Photocopiable: Contract the sentence

The aim in this activity is to reduce each sentence to ten words or less. They are all sentences containing a fairly large degree of information. One tactic here is for children to look at the words that carry the essential content of the sentence, circle these and see how they can then model them into a clear sentence.

Photocopiable: Headline the story

Drawing on the significant features of stories they know, children can create headlines that deliver information about them. By reading the results aloud they can see if others can recognize a story from their contracted headline.

Photocopiable: Could be this, could be that

Once children have isolated the meanings that are attached to each contracted sentence they could discuss which is more likely to be accepted as the meaning.

Following up

Cut out headlines: Looking at newspaper headlines, children can try figuring out what the content of the stories could be. They can swop the headlines round to see if others share their speculations.

Headline a week: Keep a diary of a week in the life of the school in headline form. Look out for events that occur and record them as headlines. Build up a chart of such headlines on a large sheet of paper forming the diary of a week.

Awkward readings: Look for examples of signs that can be misread, like those on 'Could be this, could be that'. They could be room signs on doors or signs in the street. Children can look for additional, awkward ways of misreading signs around them.

Contract the sentence

❑ Look at the sentences in the boxes. Try to contract them into smaller sentences. Try making contracted sentences of **ten** words or fewer.

The girls found the lost boy in the shop and took him to the security guard.

Girls take lost boy to security guard.

Naima fell off the swing, broke her arm and had to go to hospital.

Mr Cole, who owns the corner shop, won £1,000 in a crossword competition.

The lever came off the drinks fountain and flooded the school corridor.

Ms Holder lost her voice and couldn't teach the choir so they practised by themselves.

A taxi skidded off the road and knocked down the side wall of the playground.

The builders' scaffolding collapsed and lots of different colours of paint spattered across the wall they were painting.

The local cinema has had to close down because it is infested with rats.

Headline the story

❑ Think of a newspaper headline for each of the following stories.

The Pied Piper

Rats in stranger danger drowning

Jack and the Beanstalk

Snow White

Cinderella

Humpty Dumpty

❑ Try it with some of the other stories you know.

PHOTOCOPIABLE

Could be this, could be that

❏ Look at these sentence contractions.

DOGS MUST BE CARRIED ON THE ESCALATOR

Chop two apples with banana.

Baby Changing Room

Man burning bonfire

We smell.

PLEASE QUEUE HERE

❏ Match the possible meanings below to their contractions. There are two for each contraction. Group them together on a separate sheet of paper.

If you have a dog with you you must carry it if you use the escalator.

A room in which you can change a baby's nappy.

Chop two apples and chop a banana.

If you are making a queue this is the place to do it.

We give off a smell.

If you want to use the escalator you must be carrying a dog.

The man is burning the bonfire.

This is a bonfire for burning a man.

Use a banana to chop two apples.

We have the ability to smell odours.

Whether or not you had planned to queue we would like you to do it here.

A room in which you can swap your baby for another.

Sentence construction

Objective
Construct sentences in different ways

Language issues
Anyone who has agonized over writing a letter knows that there are numerous ways of saying the same thing. The varied ways of putting something into words may change the meaning of a sentence slightly, and the language can sound harsher or more flowery. Sentences can be extended by adding more words or can have words deleted from them. They can also be rearranged or completely different ways can be found for saying the same thing.

Ways of teaching
As children experience the varied ways in which sentences can be altered, one important aspect of this work is to encourage them to consider how they phrase the sentences they use in their day to day written work. An understanding of this aspect of grammar is what proficient writers use when they pause to consider the best way to say something.

About the activities
Photocopiable: Two sentences into one
Once children have remodelled their sentences they can compare the changes they made. The various uses of connectives can be interesting.

Photocopiable: Word count
To set the scene for this word cutting activity it may be worth asking children to imagine that they are sub-editors on a newspaper who have to try to cut the word count in this news story. A possible pared down version is shown below.

A Stanwidge puppeteer is in trouble with the authorities. Dave Kelly, whose puppet show 'Crocodella' is a favourite in Stanwidge schools has been taken to task by the Local Education Authority. Officials say the show teaches children to misbehave. In the show, Crocodella sneaks out of school to attend a ball with Prince Croc. "This is not the sort of behaviour we want to encourage," a spokesperson for the Authority said. "Truancy is a big enough problem without children seeing it promoted in a show." Dave Kelly says he is flabbergasted by the accusations. "It's just a bit of harmless fun," he says "and I am stunned anyone could think this show encourages children to behave like

Crocodella." His pleas haven't stopped education officials writing to all primary schools suggesting they do not show the show. Mr Kelly says he is working on a new show and hopes this one will be less problematic.

Photocopiable: Two for one
Children who have completed the matching of one sentence with another in this activity might also be able to offer opinions on which version of each sentence they feel is preferable.

Following up
Short news: Children can look through a selection of newspapers to find the shortest news stories and look at how much information has been put into that number of words.

Cut stories: Another activity looking at news stories involves children reading newspaper stories and seeing if they can find words that could be cut. It is not an easy task as journalism tends to involve a tight word count but it provides scope for the budding editors in the class.

Reword a paragraph: Taking a paragraph from a book, children can try to remodel it completely. This may involve the addition, removal or exchange of words or the complete rewriting of certain sentences.

Two sentences into one

You can take two short sentences:

It was raining.

Playtime was indoors.

and turn them into one, for example:

It was raining so playtime was indoors.

or:

Playtime was indoors because it was raining.

❑ Try turning these sets of two sentences into one complex sentence.

Jan's clothes were wet.

He fell in the pond.

My shoes were dirty.

I cleaned them.

The kettle boiled.

Gran made a cup of tea.

Mum dropped the mug.

It broke.

Our tortoise is hibernating.

We will bring it indoors.

Word count

❑ Here is a newspaper story. It is over 300 words long. Use a pencil to cross out words that you could delete without spoiling the story. Try to reduce the story to 175 words or less.

A children's puppeteer from Stanwidge is in big trouble with some of the officials and authorities in the town. Dave Kelly, whose puppet show 'Crocodella' has for a very long, long time been a really big favourite among young children in lots of Norwich schools has recently been seriously taken to task by the officers of the Local Education Authority. Officials say they think that the show teaches young and innocent children to misbehave. In the puppet show, 'Crocodella', it would appear, sneaks out of her school to secretly and quietly attend a palace ball and to dance with another character, the nice and attractive Prince Croc. "I can tell you now clearly and without a doubt in plain words that this is not the sort of behaviour we want to encourage in the schools of the town of Stanwidge," a spokesperson for the Authority said. "We think and really are convinced that truancy is a big enough problem without children seeing it promoted in a show, that is what we say." Dave Kelly says he is completely and totally flabbergasted by the accusations made by the officers of the Local Education Authority. "My response would be to say that it's just a bit of harmless fun," he says, "and I am stunned anyone could think this show encourages children to behave like Crocodella, the puppet who is in the story that I do in the puppet show." His desperate pleas haven't stopped the education officials of the Local Education Authority writing to all of the town's primary schools and in the letter he has written suggesting they do not show the puppet show in school. Mr Kelly says that at the moment he is currently working on a brand, spanking new show and he really, really hopes that this one will prove to be less problematic.

Two for one

The sentences below make sets of two. Each set consists of two sentences referring to the same thing. Can you match them up?

We can't go out to play because of the rain.	Loads of conkers fell out of the tree because of the ball being thrown.
Ms Kahn is ill today so Ms Porter will be teaching us.	The children were excellent during the fire practice.
James threw the ball into the tree and a load of conkers fell to the ground.	Our teacher will, today, be replaced by another teacher.
There was a fire drill at school and the children were brilliant.	The rain is preventing us from playing out.

❑ Make your own sentences in pairs, saying the same thing in different ways.

Punctuating complex sentences

Objective

Use punctuation in longer, more complex sentences

Language issues

Complex sentences are made up of more than one distinct section. Each section is called a *clause*. If a sentence states 'The cat sat on the mat', it gives a simple verbal description of where the cat performed the act of sitting. A more complex sentence might be: 'Before eating its owner, the cat sat on the mat, scratching it to shreds with those razor-like claws.' More information has been imported into this sentence: information concerning the nature of the cat, what it did to the mat and what activity preceded this action.

Main clauses are the essential part of a sentence ('The cat sat on the mat'). *Subordinate* clauses are the ones that are tagged on in order to supply further information ('Before eating it's owner', 'scratching it...' and so on) Main clauses are able to stand independently, so 'The cat sat on the mat' makes sense by itself. A subordinate clause, like 'Before eating its owner' only makes sense when tagged onto a main clause.

Ways of teaching

The addition of clauses increases the complexity of sentences, so increasing the level of punctuation required in a sentence. Simple sentences often make sense merely with a capital letter and a full stop. Add speech, raise a question or insert a clause – each of these changes requires the addition of punctuation marks.

About the activities

Photocopiable: Punctuation checklist

The checklist provides an opportunity for children to look at a range of texts they have shared in the classroom, finding examples of the main points of punctuation and reflecting on their use based on the context in which they encounter them.

Photocopiable: Sentences to redraft

The unpunctuated sentences provide an opportunity for utilizing a range of punctuation marks.

Photocopiable: Tricks page

As they find examples of the various punctuation marks in use children can try to ensure they link all of the pieces of punctuation in this text with one of the marks at the edge.

Following up

Punctuating challenge: Children can try creating a single sentence that contains the maximum number of punctuation marks they can squeeze into it.

Poster: Using the checklist (page 91) as a guide, children can try and create a poster that teaches the various punctuation points. They can include definitions of the different marks and examples of their usage.

Punctuation checklist

❑ Read sections from a text. Look for the following pieces of punctuation, ticking each one you find. Can you explain the jobs they do?
The question mark box is completed as an example.

? – " " ! , : ' ; A .

Punctuation mark	✓	Function (the job it does)
Question mark	✓	Shows that a sentence is a question.
Capital letter		
Full stop		
Speech marks		
Comma		
Exclamation mark		
Colon		
Hyphen		
Apostrophe		
Semicolon		

Sentences to redraft

❏ Rewrite these sentences, inserting the punctuation that they need in order to make sense.

are we doing art today _____

jordan said I am going to spain for my holidays and I said great I wish I could go

_____

to make pancakes you need eggs butter flour and milk

_____

on Tuesday the day after tomorrow it is lornas birthday and weve been invited to her party

_____

find these parts on the bicycle diagram the handlebars brakes saddle and wheels

_____

stop the children shouted but the bus driver who was singing to himself hadnt heard the bell

_____

can you finish your work please the teacher asked the children playtime has started

_____

sam my uncle is starting work today at my grandads cafe

_____

dont run in the corridor mr carter shouted as the children rushed out of the room

_____

Tricks page

❑ Look at this comic page and try to find the pieces of punctuation illustrated around the border. Draw a line connecting each punctuation point to an example in the text.

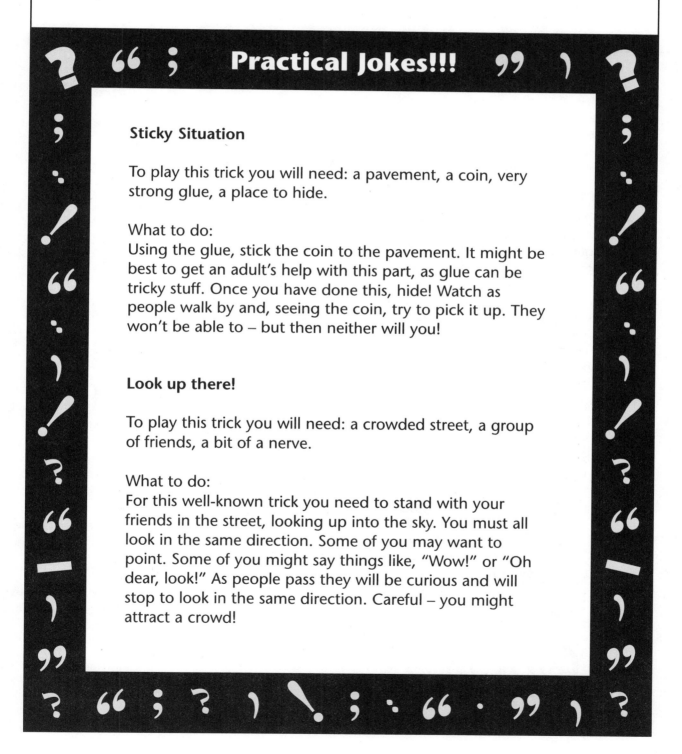

Practical Jokes!!!

Sticky Situation

To play this trick you will need: a pavement, a coin, very strong glue, a place to hide.

What to do:
Using the glue, stick the coin to the pavement. It might be best to get an adult's help with this part, as glue can be tricky stuff. Once you have done this, hide! Watch as people walk by and, seeing the coin, try to pick it up. They won't be able to – but then neither will you!

Look up there!

To play this trick you will need: a crowded street, a group of friends, a bit of a nerve.

What to do:
For this well-known trick you need to stand with your friends in the street, looking up into the sky. You must all look in the same direction. Some of you may want to point. Some of you might say things like, "Wow!" or "Oh dear, look!" As people pass they will be curious and will stop to look in the same direction. Careful – you might attract a crowd!

...dded clauses and commas

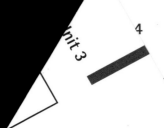

...ne comma in embedding clauses
...nces

Language issues

Clauses can be embedded within sentences providing additional information on the subject of the main clause. In the sentence 'The dog, who had caught a bad dose of fleas, scratched and scratched', the embedded clause 'having caught a bad dose of fleas' provides additional information about the dog. Such clauses are demarcated with commas. Care needs to be taken. An *embedded* clause is one that can be removed leaving a sentence that makes sense. In the above example the removal of the embedded clause leaves one in which the sense of the dog still scratching is retained.

In the sentence 'Dogs who catch fleas need powder' the words 'who catch fleas' do not constitute an embedded clause. They are part of a larger noun phrase 'Dogs who catch fleas'. The sentence is not referring to all dogs, just to a specific category (those who catch fleas).

Ways of teaching

The emphasis in this unit is upon the way in which embedded clauses can be placed within a sentence. They can also be removed without any loss of sense. The unit encourages children to look at examples of the ways in which this occurs by remodelling various complex sentences.

About the activities

Photocopiable: Embedded clause

This activity both explains and investigates the use of embedded clauses.

Photocopiable: Embedding the clause

In this activity children take a clause and locate the point at which they would embed it within a sentence.

Photocopiable: Clause matching

Part of the process of understanding when and how to place embedded clauses within a sentence involves knowing the type of clause that is demarcated in this way. This activity explores the type of clause that will be placed in specific sentences.

Following up

Clause snatching: Children can look at long and complex sentences from stories. They can write these on a white board or sheet of paper. They can look at the clauses they can remove that leave the sentence intact.

Redrafting: Ask children to look at their own writing and to record extracts that could have been presented as sentences with embedded clauses. Can they rewrite their sentences in this way?

Embedded clause

These sentences each contain a middle section that adds something to the main clause of the sentence.
So in the sentence

The dog, having caught a bad dose of fleas, scratched and scratched.

the section between commas tells us something about the dog and could be removed leaving a sentence that makes sense.
The sections in the middle are called embedded clauses and should be marked out with commas.
❏ Look at these sentences. Which words are embedded clauses? Shade over them in colouring pencil, and put commas either side of them.

My sister who starts Brownies today has new shoes.

The green door which has no window needs repairing.

My mum realizing she had no bus fare had to go back home.

Last night the school caretaker who lives in a house beside the school had to repair two broken windows.

On Tuesday after school has finished I am going swimming.

The chocolate cake which my mum had hidden had been eaten up.

My friend the one that lives in Scotland is coming to stay for a holiday.

After school if it isn't raining we are going for a picnic.

My brother without thinking about it jumped off the top diving board.

Today my bicycle which hasn't worked for weeks is going to the repair shop.

Embedding the clause

❏ Look at these sentences. They each have a strip that can be embedded somewhere in the middle of the sentence.

| The dog, | having caught a bad dose of fleas, | scratched and scratched. |

❏ Cut the strips out and stick them onto a sheet of paper. Place the embedded clauses in the sentences. Mark them out with commas.

✂ -

| My great grandmother | rides a motorbike. | who comes from Cornwall |

| My house | needs lots of repairs. | which is very old |

| You are | a great class. | I can honestly say |

| My mum | is going to have a big party. | when she celebrates her birthday |

| Our football team | is the best in our area. | having won the cup |

| My dad | comes home at weekends. | who works in London |

| Astronauts | eat food from tubes. | while out in space |

| Our cat | needs a bath. | who happens to smell |

Clause matchi

These clauses fit into the sentences below.

the one with the puncture
my mum's sister
the green one
my mother's mother
the new one
the one with the bandaged paw
the big old building
the one in the village

❑ Try to put the right clause in the right sentence.

My dog, _____, needs to see a vet.

My Gran, _____, has got false teeth.

Our school, _____, is getting knocked down.

My sister's bike, _____, needs repairing.

Today the computer, _____, broke down.

Aunty Lou, _____, is visiting us.

The old oak tree, _____, blew down in the storm.

My toothbrush, _____, has lost its bristles.

Speech and writing

~~tive~~

~~...~~stigate the difference between spoken and written
~~la~~nguage

Language issues

Speech and writing form two different modes of
communication. Speech is usually rooted in a context in
which the communicator can point or in which the items
referred to are obvious. The speaker can also use facial
expressions, so a speaker can say 'it was lovely' while
grimacing to indicate irony in their words. Writing is
rooted from its context. Standing in a car repair shop
someone asking a person in overalls 'Have you finished
with it?' is likely to be asking about the fate of his or her
car. Out of that context the written sentence 'Have you
finished with it?' remains open.

In speech a communicator can pause, use inflections
of the voice, and so on; in writing such prosody is
communicated through punctuation. In speech sentences
can be varied. Speech can be broken up and not
necessarily in complete sentences; in writing the norm is
the formation of complete sentences.

Ways of teaching

As children's writing develops, so does their grasp of the
conventions associated with this mode. Younger children
will often write in a way that does not account for the

need to communicate out of context. They will often
write exactly as they speak. In this unit the differences
between speech and writing are explored with the
intention of raising children's awareness of the
conventions that the written mode places on
communication.

About the activities

Photocopiable: Tapes and transcripts

In this activity, children tape and use speech as a starting
point for writing. They will need practice with the idea of
transcribing speech word for word but, once they have
done this, can produce the comparative forms.

Photocopiable: Transcripts

This activity builds upon the previous one, providing two
examples of text including the sorts of breaks and flows
of speech that characterize the spoken mode. The
unpunctuated and staccato nature of these texts should
contrast with the written sentences that the children
produce.

Photocopiable: Speech and Writing

The obvious difference between the speech and writing
in this activity is the number of words in the sentences.
Once they have completed this activity children can
investigate the way in which the pronouns in the spoken
form need clarification when taken out of an immediate
context and put into writing.

Following up

List the differences: Children can draw up a list of the
differences between speech and writing, comparing the
two modes. The teacher may want to refer to language
issues for the key differences they may wish to draw out
of this discussion.

Borge's punctuation: The comedian Victor Borge had an
act in which he ascribed a different sound (such as a
popping noise or raspberry) to each punctuation mark.
Children can work in groups devising their own examples
and apply these to selected sentences.

Tape adults: Children could ask for permission to tape
willing adults around the school doing things like lining
their children up and supervising dinner time and, having
produced tapes, locate sections of speech and listen for
the way these sound compared to how the same things
would be communicated in writing.

Tapes and transcripts

❑ Tape someone telling you a true short story about themselves. Listen to the tape and find a section that is really interesting in the story. In the box marked Transcript, copy out what they said, word for word. In the box marked Written sentences, put the words they use into written sentences. What sorts of changes do you make to their words?

Transcript	Written sentences

Transcripts

These transcripts show exactly what two people said when they were:
- asking for something
- recounting an event.

How would they have looked if they were written?
❑ Put each of them into written English and check the differences.

> Oh Sara listen...listen... tell you what I was thinking, like d'ya think it'd be o.k. for us to do our story on your computer cos mines all bust and my mum says it ain't gonna get fixed until after pay day and its sort of awkward cos we gotta get this thing done, yeh?

> Miss, miss, let me tell you about Saturday cos me and Carlos we found this bubble wrap and really big bubbles it was — all of it so we took us shoes and socks off and we walked all over it and, like, dug our heels in and pop pop pop it was like fireworks and then we started jumping on it and it was a real laugh.

Speech and writing

The boxes below show a spoken way and written way of saying the same thing. The spoken way is hard to understand. For example, when someone says 'What's this?' you need to be looking at them to see what they are pointing at. Can you match the spoken and written words that perform the same job?

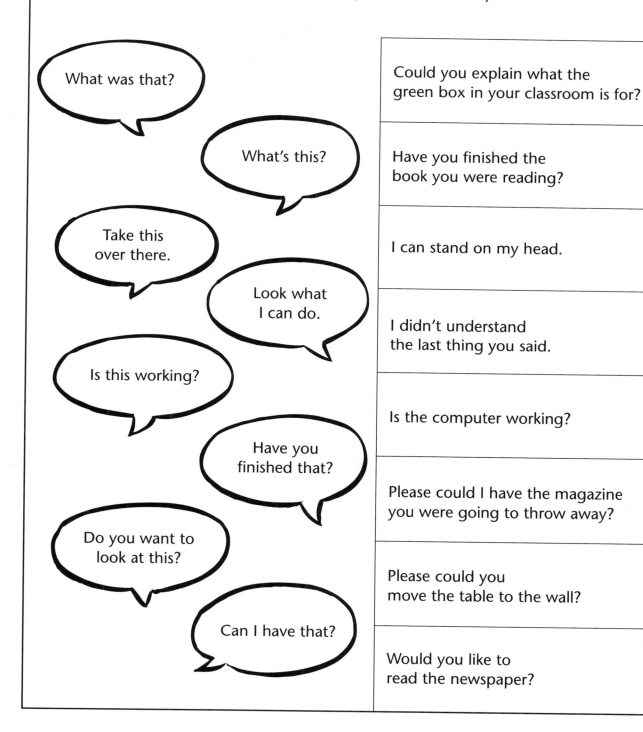

What was that?

What's this?

Take this over there.

Look what I can do.

Is this working?

Have you finished that?

Do you want to look at this?

Can I have that?

Could you explain what the green box in your classroom is for?

Have you finished the book you were reading?

I can stand on my head.

I didn't understand the last thing you said.

Is the computer working?

Please could I have the magazine you were going to throw away?

Please could you move the table to the wall?

Would you like to read the newspaper?

Clauses

Contents of Term 3a

Unit 1: Main clauses	Identify the main clause in a sentence
Unit 2: Clauses in sentences	Investigate sentences that contain more than one clause
Unit 3: Connectives	Understand how clauses are connected
Unit 4: Using connectives	Use connectives to link clauses and sentences
Unit 5: Understanding clauses	Understand the use of clauses

This half-term

It may seem odd to give a whole half-term over to one aspect of grammar; however, the units in this half-term introduce clauses, taking children through one of the most awkward themes of grammar that they will encounter in Key Stage 2.

Poster notes

Clauses and sentences
The definitions and examples on this poster are not enough to clarify the different ways clauses can feature in sentences. The poster is therefore a reference point for the teacher to explain the idea. Units 1 and 2 contain ideas to develop children's understanding of this area.

Connectives
This poster reinforces the poster in the half-term section 2b. It provides an outline of the four types of connective and the functions they perform.

Clauses and sentences

Simple sentences contain one clause:

The cat slept.

Compound sentences contain clauses of equal importance.

The cat slept and the dog ate.

Complex sentences contain a main clause and a subordinate clause.

The cat woke up because the dog barked.

Connectives

Add one clause to another

for example,
I like rain and I like snow.

Oppose one clause against another

for example,
I like rain but my friend hates it.

Show how one clause is caused by another

for example,
I like snow because it looks great.

Show how one clause is linked to the time of another

for example, **we put on warm clothes then we went out in the snow.**

Scholastic Literacy Skills
Grammar and punctuation

Main clauses

Objective
Identify the main clause in a sentence

Language issues
Clauses are units of language that make sense in themselves. They can be *whole* sentences, such as 'The cat slept', or they can feature *within* sentences. Within sentences they feature as distinct elements with verbs of their own. In a sentence like 'The cat slept even though the orchestra played because they didn't disturb it', there are three distinct clauses:

    'The cat slept'
    'the orchestra played'
    'they didn't disturb it'.

Each of these clauses could make a discrete, short sentence. In this sentence the *main* clause is 'The cat slept', while the other two provide information about the cat sleeping, and are therefore *subordinate* clauses.

Ways of teaching
As a means of reinforcing the concept of clauses to the class, this unit asks children to look for the main clause in lengthy sentences. As they do this children need to bear in mind that a main clause is very much like a sentence in itself.

About the activities
Photocopiable: What is the sentence about?
As children undertake this activity one way of focusing upon the main clause in each sentence is to ask what the main event is in each of the examples given.

Photocopiable: Find the main clause
This activity involves children trimming sentences to isolate the main clause. Once they have done this they can also look at the elements of the sentence left over at the end of the activity, asking themselves what job these do and seeing if they can find leftovers that have something in common (such as explaining why an event occurred).

Photocopiable: Sentence repairs
In this activity children match the clauses together to rebuild a broken sentence. Once they have done this they could reflect on which parts of the rebuilt sentence can stand independently. For example, in 'Shona had a leaving party so that we could all say "Goodbye" to her', the first half of the sentence makes sense on its own: 'Shona had a leaving party' whereas the second half does not: 'so that we could all say "Goodbye" to her'. The first half is the main clause. The second half is a subordinate clause that explains the reason behind the party.

Following up
Roundabout way of saying: Children could try to devise their own sentences in the style of the examples shown in 'What is the sentence about?' They can try to find a plain sentence and to create a long, flowery version of the same thing.

Plain words: Ask children to find examples of flowery ways of saying something, either in texts that they have read or ones that their parents receive. Junk mail makes an excellent starting point for this, as it tends to be verbose while saying very little!

What is the sentence about?

Here are some very long sentences. Can you write a shorter sentence that says the main thing from the bigger sentence? You might remove bits from:

the beginning	or the middle	or the end
Realizing I had nothing else to do for the time being I played with my friend.	*I, having thought and thought about what I could do to fill a space of time available to me, played with my friend.*	*I played with my friend because I really, really wanted to more than anything else in the world.*

I played with my friend.

❑ Write your shortened sentences in the space provided.

Long version	Shortened version
The tree, which for many years had stood outside the school gate beside the road, fell over.	The tree fell over.
As part of an assembly to celebrate the start of the new school year Caroline sang a song.	
Before visiting us to celebrate my birthday my Uncle made a cake.	
I played with my friend, which is hardly surprising, because I do that every day after school.	
It was, without any shadow of a doubt, raining.	
Sam swallowed his tooth although he was not made ill by this accident.	
The caretaker mended our window which is good because it was broken and needed mending.	
There was, during the afternoon of Thursday the 1st of September, a thunderstorm.	

Find the main clause

In long sentences there is usually a main clause. It is the main thing the sentence is about. In a sentence like

> *The cat slept even though the orchestra played because they didn't disturb it.*

the main clause is

The cat slept

The other bits of the sentence add more information about the main clause.

the orchestra played		*they didn't disturb it*

Main clauses sometimes look like little sentences inside bigger sentences. Cut each main clause out of these sentences.

After tea my mum watches telly because she likes the news.

The boy fell off the swing although he wasn't injured.

I saw a good film at the cinema that I hadn't seen before.

If it's open we are going to the library so that we can change our books.

I am watching the kettle until it boils.

Open the window so that we can get some fresh air.

It is time to clear up unless you want to stay in after school.

When the bell rings we can go out to play unless it is raining.

Sentence repairs

❑ Match the beginnings and endings of the sentences below.

Without checking he had his bus fare

my brother wore his wet trainers.

The classroom was messy

Sam ran to catch the bus.

It was sunny

so our teacher was not pleased.

We made sandwiches

until we changed at half time.

By next Tuesday

so that we could all say 'Goodbye' to her.

After thinking about it for ages

my bike will be mended.

Because of the rain

my Dad decided to have a hair cut.

Even after he had been told not to

because we were having a picnic.

Shona had a leaving party

although the forecast predicted rain.

Ali was in goal

our trip was cancelled.

Clauses in sentences

Objective
Investigate sentences that contain more than one clause

Language issues
Sentences can feature various combinations of clauses of different types. *Simple* sentences contain one clause:
> *The cat slept.*

Compound sentences contain more than one clause. In compound sentences the clauses are of equal importance. Each clause is like a sentence in itself and neither can be picked out as the main clause:
> *The cat slept and the dog ate.*
> *The dog ate and the cat slept and the hamster knitted and the fish dived.*

In *complex* sentences there is a main clause and a subordinate clause, the latter being, in some way, dependent upon the main clause in order to make sense:
> *The cat woke up because the dog barked.*

Ways of teaching
The main focus of this unit should be the distinguishing and picking apart of one clause from another. This can involve looking at different types of clause.

About the activities
Photocopiable: Two clauses
In this activity children are asked to separate the two clauses in a sentence. Remind them that one way of doing this is by locating the verbs in a sentence. Remind them that clauses are like mini-sentences. Once they have completed the activity they can look at the way in which some clauses are subordinate to others.

Photocopiable: Create a complexity
Using various clauses this activity requires children to create obscure sentences. They can add capital letters and full stops to these and keep a record of some of the more difficult constructions they devise.

Photocopiable: Clause count
Children use this table to look at the clauses in complex and compound sentences. Once they have written the sentence into the second column they may find it useful to shade over the clauses using different coloured pencils.

Following up
Most clauses: Children can look in texts available in the classroom with the challenge of trying to find the sentence that contains the greatest number of clauses.

Cutting out sentences: Using disposable texts, such as leaflets and adverts, children can cut up the sentences they find into separate clauses.

Sentence shuffle: Children can try making their own sets of clauses like the ones used in 'Create a complexity'. The key thing here is to include some wayward and obscure clauses so that when the shuffling around takes place strange sentences start to appear.

Two clauses

Each of these sentences contains two clauses.

❏ Write each clause in the spaces underneath the sentence.

The car stopped because it ran out of petrol.

After we finished dinner we went out to play.

Ahmed is seven today so we are having a party.

I like lemonade but my mum can't stand it.

Create a complexity

❏ Using the clauses below make up some long and strange sentences – for example, *My dog fell off the wall because of my Granny's teeth.*
❏ Put in the correct punctuation for each of your sentences.

my dog fell off the wall

the burglar ran away

my mum was sad

at a café beside the sea

and they went all over the table

because she spun round and round

when she saw a cat

because of my Granny's teeth

which she lost at Cleethorpes

while eating a bowl of Cornflakes

while scratching his fleas

inside the teacher's desk

in the middle of the night

with a jam sponge

Aunty Louisa sneezed

which really belonged to my neighbour

I fell in the pool

wearing a pair of bright green trunks

so that he wouldn't get caught

and she started to cry

Clause count

❑ Using the table below copy out a long sentence from a text. Make a note of the text you use. Make a note of the number of clauses you can find in the sentence. Give an example of **one** separate clause.

Text	Sentence	No.	Example
Letter home from school	During the winter months, particularly when nights are dark, we are making special arrangements for parents so that children don't have to wait in the playground to be collected.	5	so that children don't have to wait in the playground

Connectives

Objective
Understand how clauses are connected

Language issues
Clauses can be connected together in various ways in order to make a simple into a complex or compound sentence. Connections can indicate the relationship between two clauses. The main connections involve:
❑ *addition*: one clause adding information to another, linked by words like 'and' and 'also' – such as 'The dog barked and the cat ran'.
❑ *opposition*: one clause contradicting or standing in opposition to another, linked by words like 'but', 'yet' and 'though' – such as 'The dog barked but the cat stayed asleep'.
❑ *cause*: one clause caused by another, linked by words like 'because' and 'therefore' – such as 'The cat woke up because the dog barked'.
❑ *time*: one clause in a temporal relationship with another, linked by words like 'then' and 'after' – such as 'The dog barked then the cat woke up'.

Ways of teaching
As they encounter the various connectives in this unit children should familiarize themselves with the use of various words to connect clauses. This involves having some idea of the different ways in which clauses can be connected.

About the activities
Photocopiable: Choose the connective
As they create sentences using the parts shown on the photocopiable page, children have to consider the most appropriate connective to link two clauses. This will involve understanding the relationship between the two clauses and finding an appropriate word.

Photocopiable: Find the connectives
Using their awareness of the different functions performed by connectives, children can sort the sentences shown into four groups according to whether the connectives make their link using addition, opposition, cause or time. To begin the task children should locate and circle the connective.

Photocopiable: Use the connective
This activity presents a wider range of connectives that children can try to use in sentences of their own devising.

Following up
Analysing leaflets: Collect information leaflets from a variety of sources and ask children to read through them finding the different connective words that appear.

New connective: The class can choose a connective to promote. They can try to slip it into their speech and writing. If, for example, they adopt the word 'furthermore' then they have to use it as often as possible.

Find other ones: Looking through various texts, children can try to find new connectives and keep a list of them. These could also be classified according to the function they perform.

Choose the connective

❏ Look at the sentence parts below. Choose starters, connectives and finishers that fit together and make sentences.

Starters	Connective	Finishers
I like football	but	I had my tea.
First I went home	and	it boiled.
I went to the park	also	I don't like cricket.
I set out for school	after	my friend came too.
We went to the fair	then	she moans too much.
Our teacher is grumpy	so that	I could buy a new game.
I saved my pocket money	because	I had finished my breakfast.
The steam came out of the kettle	however	the roller coaster was closed.

❏ Make up your own sentences using a starter, a connective and a finisher.

_____

_____

_____

_____

_____

_____

_____

_____

Find the connectives

Connectives are words or phrases that link parts of a text together. They are often used to connect clauses.

Addition	Opposition	Cause	Time
add one clause to another:	show one clause in opposition to another:	show how one clause is caused by another:	show how one clause is linked to the time of another:
for example: *I like rain* and *I like snow.*	for example: *I like sun* but *I hate rain.*	for example: *I like snow* because *it looks great.*	for example: *We put on warm clothes* then *went out in the snow.*

❑ Sort these sentences according to the job the connective is doing. Remember, the connective can come anywhere in the sentence.

We did some writing after we finished art.

The television made a noise because it was broken.

We are going swimming and we are going skating.

We were going to go out but we had to tidy up.

The children lined up before going into school.

The hinges are loose so the door won't open.

The roof is leaking, also the window is broken.

I thought we were doing art, however we are doing PE.

We'll have to tidy up which means we'll miss playtime.

The kettle boiled and the toast popped out of the toaster.

Use the connective

❑ Write a sentence using each of the connectives shown in the table below.

Connective	Sentence
so that	We will switch on the heating so that we can be warm.
because	
then	
and also	
furthermore	
consequently	
as a result	
on the other hand	
meanwhile	
but	
instead of	

Using connectives

Objective
Use connectives to link clauses and sentences

Language issues
Clauses can be connected using various words and phrases (as well as punctuation features such as colons and commas). When it comes to words and phrases the connectives used will vary according to the relationship between clauses. In a compound sentence (one in which the clauses are of equal importance) the connecting words will tend to be words like 'and' or 'then'. In a complex sentence the connecting words will subordinate one clause to another, making one the explanation of another, with words like 'because' and 'therefore'.

Ways of teaching
Children should expand the number of connectives they can draw upon in their own writing by examining their use in sentences. Care should be taken to avoid any idea that longer sentences are inherently better. Children need to be aware that they are being given the ability to construct these should they be of use. However, a short sentence can be just as useful in the right context.

Connectives form one of the main ways in which a text has cohesion. Different text types tend to draw a lot on particular connecting words. A narrative text will draw upon temporal connectives whereas an explanatory text may draw upon causal connectives in constructing explanations.

About the activities
Photocopiable: Same start, different ending...
Using the different connectives should cause children to produce different sentence endings. The various sentences can be discussed to examine how the function of the connectives steered the various sentences in particular ways.

Photocopiable: Connecting words
This activity asks children to seek out the connectives in a story from Terry Jones's *Fairy Tales*. This could lead to a discussion of the function the connectives perform. Note that this activity points out connectives working within and across sentences.

Connectives used in the story: and, but, so, therefore, before.

Photocopiable: Short and long sentences
Drawing on a selection of short, single clause sentences, children are asked to create longer, complex and compound examples. One aspect of this activity worth following up is the use of connectives. Children will use various connectives depending on the relationship between the clauses.

Following up
Connective challenge: Challenge the children to produce a sentence that uses four different connectives. They should each be performing one of the functions of connectives.

Text marking: Using leaflets and cuttings children can find connectives and circle them, then draw links joining them to the clauses and sentences they join.

Same start, different ending...

❑ Using the sentence starters below, complete the sentences. The first one is done for you.

The girl opened the box after	*the postman had given it to her.*
The girl opened the box so that	
The girl opened the box and	
The girl opened the box but	
We enjoy playtime but	
We enjoy playtime, on the other hand	
We enjoy playtime because	
We enjoy playtime after	
The magician appeared however	
The magician appeared in order that	
The magician appeared meanwhile	
The magician appeared and also	

How does the connective affect the way you finish the sentence?

Connecting words

Connecting words can make links within sentences.

They can also make links across sentences, linking one sentence

We had our tea.

with another

We had our tea.	After that	we played outside

❑ Look for the connecting words in this story. What function is each of them performing?

Three Raindrops

A raindrop was falling out of a cloud, and it said to the raindrop next to it: 'I'm the biggest and best raindrop in the whole sky!'

'You are indeed a fine raindrop,' said the second, 'but you are not nearly so beautifully shaped as I am. And in my opinion it's shape that counts, and *I* am therefore the best raindrop in the whole sky.'

The first raindrop replied: 'Let us settle this matter once and for all.' So they asked a third raindrop to decide between them.

But the third raindrop said: 'What nonsense you're both talking! *You* may be a big raindrop, and *you* are certainly well shaped, but, as everybody knows, it's purity that really counts, and I am purer than either of you. *I* am therefore the best raindrop in the whole sky!'

Well, before either of the other raindrops could reply, they all three hit the ground and became part of a very muddy puddle.

Terry Jones

Short and long sentences

❑ Look at these short sentences.

We are not happy.	We helped the dinner supervisors.	We will show our parents.	We are working together.
We can't go outside.	We have nearly finished.	We are making a display.	We co-operated.
We have to tidy up.	The bell rang.	We are working very hard.	We go to dinner.
Our teacher asked us to help.	We didn't finish our work.	We are enjoying ourselves.	We finished our work.
It is raining outside.	We are practising a play.	We finished our pictures.	We are waiting for the bell.

❑ Use these short sentences as clauses in longer sentences. Try using two short sentences to make each long sentence. You can use any connecting words needed between the clauses, for example:

> *We helped the dinner supervisors until the bell rang.*

_____

_____

_____

_____

_____

_____

_____

_____

Understanding clauses

Objective
Understand the use of clauses

Language issues
Clauses make up the small units of sense within a sentence. In complex and compound sentences they can be combined using connectives. The complexity of a text lies, in part, in the nature of the sentences. Simple sentences are often easy to interpret. However, from a stylistic point of view, complex and compound sentences can make text flow in a more readable way.

Ways of teaching
This unit steps beyond the basic understanding of clauses by encouraging children to use their awareness of this aspect of grammar. They can play with clauses and pick sentences apart. They can also examine the clause structure of different texts.

About the activities
Photocopiable: The sub-clause
This activity asks children to look at the sub-clause in various sentences. It is worth remembering that a main clause is one that can stand on its own whereas a sub-clause is dependent upon the main clause to make sense.

Photocopiable: Sentences in story books
Reading books can provide interesting material for this exercise as they constitute a type of text in which clause structure is given a fair deal of consideration. However, care should be taken not to turn this activity into a belittling of texts at the earliest stages of the reading scheme.

Photocopiable: Inserting clauses
This activity encourages children to lengthen sentences to ridiculous degrees. They may wish to write their additions in variously coloured felt-tipped pens to give the whole thing a bit of colour.

Following up
Well-known sentences: Well-known (and well-worn) sentences, such as 'Time flies when you're having fun', can be adapted by inserting clauses to see how they can be changed.

Reading book: Quite often at Key Stage 2 children undertake the task of producing a story for children to read at Key Stage 1. Their understanding of clauses can be used to help them produce simple sentence books.

Gobbledegook Prize: The class can set up a hunt for the most confusing and complicated sentence in any text. It could be a letter or a passage from a text book. When they find the worst example they can award it the Gobbledegook Prize.

The sub-clause

❑ Looking at each of the sentences below, copy out the words that make up sub-clauses.

My mum, who's a vet, works in the city.

Josh found, after trying and
trying, he could swim a whole length.

The children made a cake
because they were having a party.

If you want a good laugh
you should read my story.

After writing their stories
the children made a play.

The girl looked for her shoes,
having lost them in the classroom.

If the weather improves
we can play rounders.

When the clock says three o'clock
we can pack up for home time.

Before going into
assembly we have to line up.

Our teacher, a very
scruffy man, wore a tie today.

Sentences in story books

❑ Look at a selection of story books. Out of **ten** sentences in each book:
- how many are **simple** sentences?
- how many are **compound** sentences?
- how many are **complex** sentences?

Book title	Out of ten sentences		
	Number of simple sentences	Number of compound sentences	Number of complex sentences

Inserting clauses

❏ Cut these simple sentences up. Make clauses to extend them. Write these new clauses on strips of paper and tape them into the simple sentence. For example:

Could become

or

Prepositions, apostrophes & punctua

Contents of Term 3b

Unit 1: **Introducing prepositions**	Identify prepositions
Unit 2: **Understanding prepositions**	Experiment with a range of prepositions
Unit 3: **Using prepositions**	Experiment with the use of prepositions
Unit 4: **Apostrophe of possession**	Revise the use of apostrophe for possession
Unit 5: **Punctuating complex sentences**	Use punctuation marks accurately in complex sentences

This half-term

The small class of words called *prepositions* perform essential tasks in the English language. They are introduced in this half-term. They tend to be relatively easy to identify and children quickly grasp their function. The half-term also includes work on apostrophes of possession and punctuation.

Poster notes

Prepositions
The list of prepositions is not exhaustive but provides examples of common words that perform this function.

Punctuation notes
The poster shows the various punctuation marks performing their function. It can provide a discussion point as children find the various marks in their relevant sentences and look at the function they are performing, for example what is being tagged on by the dash.

Prepositions

towards   behind

for   under

while

except for

in front of

through

into

before   **since**

ABOUT

between

out of

across   away from

because of   after

instead of   against

Punctuation notes

apital letter at start of sentence

Dash to tag bits onto a sentence ⸺ like this.

Full stop to end a sentence ₒ

What does a question mark do ?

The teacher said " *Speech marks demarcate speech.* "

Comma to separate clauses, items in a list, that sort of thing.

Wow – exclamation mark !

Colon to introduce a list : and introduce a second clause.

Semicolons provide stronger pauses than commas ; they separate clauses like this.

Apostrophes show a noun's possession or they show contraction.

ntroducing prepositions

Language issues

Prepositions are words or phrases that indicate when or where something is in relation to something else. They are, as the word implies, position words that come before other words. They usually appear before a noun or a pronoun. In a sentence like 'The cow jumped over the moon' the preposition 'over' explains where the cow jumped in relation to the moon (as opposed to 'under' or 'through' it). There is a limited number of prepositions in the English language. A survey of words that have been added to the language will show a growth in certain word types such as nouns and verbs. The number of prepositions, on the other hand, tends to remain stable.

Ways of teaching

The crucial aspect of work on prepositions is to enable children to identify them. They will use most of them already, and will be able to read and write many. In this unit they identify the prepositions they know.

About the activities

Photocopiable: Listing prepositions

This activity asks children to list all the prepositions they can think of. As they undertake this the teacher may wish to let them look in various texts such as story books, newspapers and instruction leaflets in order to find examples.

Photocopiable: Find the prepositions

Looking at the text, children have to find the prepositions. Remind them that prepositions are about more than just place – they can indicate time as well.

Photocopiable: The drawing game

Using the strips on the photocopiable page children work in twos. One should be the leader and the other the follower. The leader draws a route from the start to the finish of the strip. They can be fairly elaborate about this, going back on themselves, up and down and through the shapes, but they must not let the follower see their route. Once the leader has completed their route they have to sit so that they cannot see the follower's strip and vice versa. They then have to use directions to instruct the follower how to get from start to finish, using the same line. This will involve using prepositions, for example 'over', 'between', 'around'. Once the route is complete they can compare strips to see how well the follower did.

Following up

The exhaustive guide: The class can turn their own efforts at preposition recognition into a whole-class list to which they all contribute.

Dictionary hunting: Ask the children to work in groups, looking through the dictionary a page at a time finding any prepositions they can. This may add to the list being drawn up by the class.

Shared reading: The book *Rosie's Walk* is an ever popular children's story (*Rosie's Walk* by Pat Hutchins, ISBN 0-14-050032-4, Puffin, 1968). It also provides an entertaining example of a story that uses a range of prepositions in describing Rosie's walk across and through various features of the farmyard.

Your route to school: Children can write out the directions of their walk to school, trying to use as many prepositions as they can. At first it may seem difficult to use a preposition like 'under' but when encouraged to incorporate it they will recall telephone wires or street signs 'under' which they pass.

Listing prepositions

Prepositions are words that can show the link between two things.

- They could be linked in time
  for example:

I had breakfast before school.

- or space

Put the jigsaw in the box.

- or in another way

This cake is for Gran.

How many prepositions can you think of?

nd the prepositions

...e prepositions in these directions?

Travel by boat up the river towards the windmill. Stop beside the windmill and walk behind it. Walk across the field into the wood. Carefully pass through the wood until you see the arch. Before going through the archway check you are not being followed. Go under the arch and through the tunnel. You will come out by the old oak tree. After reaching the oak tree walk down the hill and over the stream. Near the stream you will see a house on a hill. Go to the door, the key is under the mat, and step inside...

The drawing game

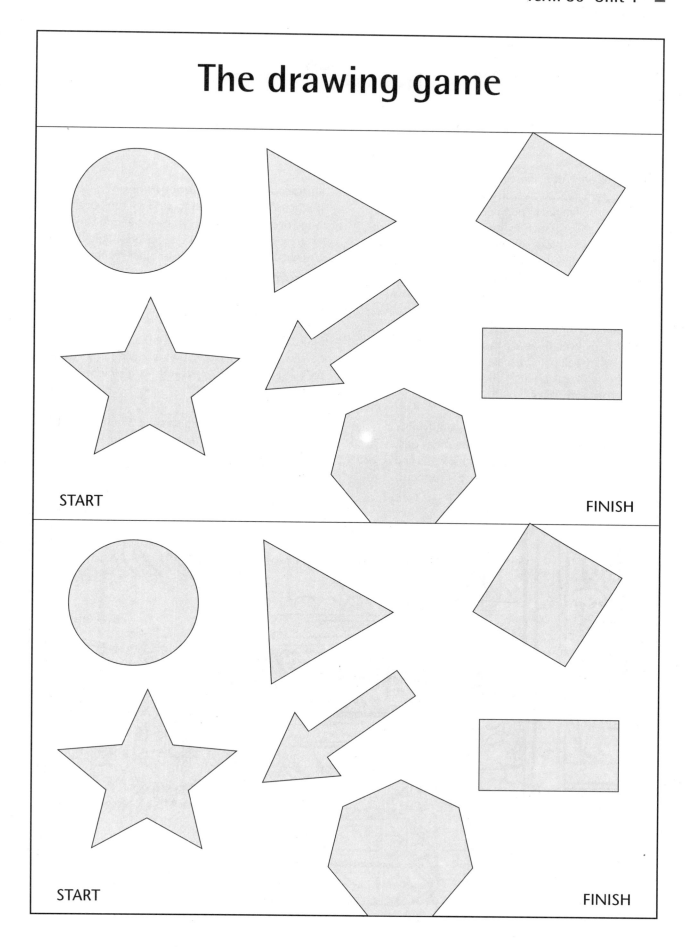

START   FINISH

START   FINISH

Understanding prepositions

Objective
Experiment with a range of prepositions

Language issues
Prepositions are crucial words in relating the links between grammatical ideas. They tend to be short words, and are limited in number. Prepositions can consist of one word, such as 'over', 'at', or 'before' or two words, such as 'out of' and 'away from'. There are also complex prepositions that are made up of three words, such as 'in front of' and 'on top of'.

Ways of teaching
Prepositions constitute a limited category of words rarely added to. However, there is a range of words here that children can develop and expand in their own writing.

About the activities
Photocopiable: Preposition cutting
One way of approaching the task of identifying a class of word within a sentence is to eliminate other classes. In this activity children cut out any nouns, verbs and so on, leaving behind words they think are prepositions.

Photocopiable: Preposition spaces
This cloze activity will involve children in examining the context of the story in order to decide which preposition best fits the newspaper article.

Photocopiable: Using prepositions
This activity asks children to produce sentences that use a range of prepositions. It can be made more challenging by suggesting to children that, as they write their sentences, they may include another preposition not shown on the photocopiable.

Following up
Preposition cards: Write some prepositions on a set of ten cards. Ask children to place the cards face downwards and take turns at removing three cards from the pile and making a sentence with whichever prepositions they select.

Word count: Children can sort the various prepositions they find and use according to the number of words they contain.

Preposition cutting

❑ Read these sentences carefully. Cross out all the words that are **not** prepositions. Make a list of the prepositions you are left with.

Gran left her bicycle against the railings in front of the library.

She went into the library and as far
as she was concerned the bike was safely parked outside.

After half an hour she came out of the library.

Alongside the railings there was nothing except for the bicycle pump.

Gran looked all around and saw someone riding away on her bike.

She ran after the thief and caught up with him near to the market.

In spite of the fact he was twice as big as her, she ran
towards him and knocked him off the bike with the pump.

He jumped over the wall and ran off through the market.

Preposition spaces

❏ Look at the newspaper article below. Prepositions have been removed from the text. Can you think of a word that would fit each of the spaces? Remember, prepositions can be one or two words or more.

Hands _____ the water

_____ weeks _____ preparation, Martina Hands, a teacher _____ Balstone Junior, is ready _____ a challenging ordeal. Martina plans to sail _____ the English Channel _____ a home-made raft. The raft is made _____ recycled materials and has been trialled _____ all types of water, _____ the Channel. This Saturday raft and Channel meet for the first time, battling _____ themselves to see who will win.

Martina is confident the raft will hold _____ wind and rain. She will be protected _____ a tarpaulin but says she will still wrap up well.

Martina has always been a keen sailor. _____ teaching she was _____ the navy. She said "I've been _____ difficult journeys and am looking forward _____ this one. But I hope I'm not _____ school for too long."

Boxing match

Fruit seller, Carl Hall, is furious _____ council plans to stop his long-standing practice of stacking fruit boxes _____ his shop. Council officials say his boxes are obstructing the pavement, where they are arranged. "I am furious," said Carl. "I have displayed goods _____ the canopy

_____ my shop _____ years and _____ this I have never had any complaints." Pointing to the pavement he says "There is plenty of room _____ boxes and the road. I can't see what all the fuss is _____."

Council spokesperson said "Mr Hall has ample room to display goods _____ his shop window. We don't want a fuss _____ a couple of boxes." But Carl plans to appeal _____ the council's decision.

Using prepositions

❑ Try writing sentences in the space provided using both the prepositions.

instead of	Instead of just standing beside it, we jumped into the pool.
into	
except for	
about	
away from	
between	
across	
because of	
in front of	
before	
through	
after	
against	
since	
towards	
out of	
while	
behind	
under	
for	

Using prepositions

Objective
Experiment with the use of prepositions

Language issues
Two of the most significant functions of prepositions are to show relationships of space, such as 'over' and 'near', or time, such as 'before' and 'after'. Prepositions can also indicate possession ('The house of my uncle') or they can show other links between nouns ('I want coffee instead of tea').

Ways of teaching
Prepositions are relatively bland words. Nevertheless, there is some consideration to be given to which ones are best used in particular contexts. Throughout this unit children explore the range of prepositions they could use in a variety of ways.

About the activities
Photocopiable: Possible Prepositions
Certain prepositions perform certain tasks. Looking at the context in these sentences children can try figuring out what job could be performed by which prepositions.

Photocopiable: Playtime
This photocopiable should be enlarged to A3 size so that the children can use it to produce sentences describing what is taking place in the playground. They can try to use a wide range of prepositions. For example, is the girl just 'on' the climbing frame or could she be said to be climbing 'over' the bars?

Photocopiable: Pop
Using the Rosen poem as a guide to preposition use, children can use various imperatives to produce their own poem in a similar vein.

Following up
Big pictures: Try and obtain a large picture in which a lot is taking place, such as a modern cartoon poster or a print of a classic picture (Brueghel's 'Children's Games' is good for this). Ask children to point things out and notice how they use prepositions in exploring such pictures.

Comic stories: Looking at three pictures from a comic story, ask children to write sentences about the scenes using a variety of prepositions. Remind them that they can write using time prepositions ('before', 'after') as well as spatial ones ('over', 'through').

Directions: Tape an adult giving directions. Replay the tape and note the prepositions used. Which ones are the most common?

Possible prepositions

❑ Look at these sentences and list **two** prepositions that could fill the spaces.

We had something to eat _____ playing outside.

Wash the paint pots _____ playtime.

The football was _____ the shelf.

I found my pencil _____ the book.

You can use a pencil _____ a pen.

Put the bottle _____ the sink.

I met Joe _____ the library.

Playtime

❑ Write **eight** sentences describing parts of this scene. Try using a range of prepositions.

Pop

❏ Read this poem by Michael Rosen.

Busy Day

Pop in
pop out
pop over the road
pop out for a walk
pop in for a talk
pop down to the shop
can't stop
got to pop

got to pop?

pop where?
pop what?

well
I've got to
pop round
pop up
pop in to town
pop out and see
pop in for tea
pop down to the shop
can't stop
got to pop

got to pop?

pop where?
pop what?

well
I've got to
pop in
pop out
pop over the road
pop out for a walk
pop in for a talk.....

Michael Rosen

❏ Notice how many different prepositions are used. Could you write a similar poem using a range of prepositions after a verb?

Apostrophe of possession

Objective
Revise the use of apostrophe for possession

Language issues
Apostrophes can be used to show possession. An apostrophe on a noun shows that it possesses a following item – for example 'Sean's book'. Rules for adding apostrophes depend upon the noun to which it is being added.

If the noun is singular and doesn't end in 's' you add an apostrophe and an 's', for example:

Sam's dog.

If the noun is singular and ends in 's' you add an apostrophe and an 's', for example:

Ross's dog
Paris's tower.

If the noun is plural and doesn't end in 's' you add an apostrophe and an 's', for example:

the children's dog
the mice's nest.

If the noun is plural and ends in 's' you add an apostrophe but *don't* add an 's', for example:

the babies' rattles
the teachers' mugs.

Ways of teaching
This unit presents a brief review of the use of the apostrophe. Emphasis is placed upon the way in which it is added to a noun to show possession.

Noun grid		
singular	*eg Sam*	*eg Ross*
plural	*eg children*	*eg babies*
	doesn't end in 's'	ends in 's'

About the activities
Photocopiable: Noun grid
The grid looks at the way nouns are classified when apostrophes are being added. Children cut out the nouns shown and sort them onto the Carroll diagram, matching the column and row to place nouns correctly. By placing nouns on the grid children are making the sort of classification they will use when they add apostrophes.

Photocopiable: Placing apostrophes
This activity presents a review of the rules for using the apostrophe. Children then use these in placing apostrophes in the sentences shown.

Photocopiable: Apostrophes in sentences
As they use the nouns shown in a possessive form in sentences, children will need to consider how the noun endings take the apostrophe.

Following up
Apostrophe use: Children can look at their own use of the apostrophe in recent work, possibly using the 'Noun grid' to analyse words they have used. They can check the correctness of their placing of the apostrophe.

Noun grid

Carroll diagram

	does not end in 's'	ends in 's'
singular		
plural		

✂

Kate	Ross	Mr Harris

woman

dog	Paris	geese

children	mice	geese	fishes

Sam	peoples	dogs	women

Placing apostrophes

Here are the rules for the use of apostrophes.

If the noun is singular and doesn't end in 's' you add an apostrophe and an 's', for example: *Sam's dog.*	If the noun is singular and ends in 's' you add an apostrophe and an 's', for example: *Ross's dog* *Paris's tower.*
If the noun is plural and doesn't end in 's' you add an apostrophe and an 's', for example: *the children's dog* *the mice's nest.*	If the noun is plural and ends in 's' you add an apostrophe but *don't* add an 's', for example: *the babies' rattles* *the teachers' mugs.*

❏ Rewrite these sentences using apostrophes.

The fishes water was cleaned. _____

We mended Grans window. _____

Mr Thomass classroom is untidy. _____

Liams mum is a doctor. _____

My schools playtime is in the morning. _____

The womens meeting is postponed. _____

The thieves plans were devious. _____

My classs assembly is on Tuesday. _____

I flew Ryans kite. _____

This shop sells mens clothes. _____

The childrens teacher ran away. _____

Apostrophes in sentences

❑ Look at this list of owners.

Prime Minister	dragons	leopard	bookseller
teacher	children	babies	cook
cows	hippopotamuses	firefighter	princess

❑ Think of an item each of them could own. Write a sentence about them and the item that they own. Use an apostrophe to show that they own the item.

_____

_____

_____

_____

_____

_____

_____

_____

_____

_____

Punctuating complex sentences

Objective
Use punctuation marks accurately in complex sentences

Language issues
This unit revises some of the main points of punctuation of which children should be developing an understanding, notably:
- ❑ capital letter at the start of a sentence
- ❑ full stop to end a sentence
- ❑ question mark to denote a question
- ❑ speech marks to demarcate speech
- ❑ comma to separate clauses and items in a list
- ❑ exclamation mark to show an exclamation
- ❑ colon to introduce a list or to introduce a second clause
- ❑ semicolon to provide a stronger pause than a comma, separating clauses
- ❑ apostrophe to show possession or contraction
- ❑ dash to tag clauses onto a sentence or to use around a parenthetical clause.

About the activities
Photocopiable: Sentence looping
The correct use of punctuation involves being familiar with certain aspects of sentences. In this activity children use colouring pencils to demarcate some of the significant aspects of sentences that are punctuated in particular ways. Their looping of speech develops awareness of where they should place speech marks. The looping of clauses develops an understanding of where they should place clause-separating items of punctuation such as commas and colons. Awareness of questions develops use of the question mark.

Photocopiable: Punctuation hunt
As they look for examples of punctuation children should develop their understanding of the actual uses of the various types of punctuation revised in this unit.

Photocopiable: In this sentence...
The lists to the side of the sentences in this activity give children a clear idea of the punctuation they can insert into the sentences.

Following up
Revision: Children can try to make up their own examples of how each of the punctuation marks covered in this unit would be put to use.

Revisiting writing: Children can look back at their writing over the course of the school year and look at how their use of punctuation has developed.

Sentence looping

❏ Look at the unpunctuated sentences below and circle different bits in
different colours.
- Circle words that are spoken in red.
- Circle sub-clauses in green.
- Circle sentences that are questions in blue.

louise said help me do this jigsaw

is it time for dinner

on Tuesday after school finishes we go to club

lola said lets go ice skating next friday

the teacher said its time for our spelling test

after thinking for a while sam said lets go to my house

we went to blackpool which was a big treat

can you play a cd on this player

our class decided after a lot of thinking to have a party

Punctuation hunt

❏ Look through newspapers, leaflets and magazines and try to find examples of the following pieces of punctuation. Cut them out and stick them in the table.

full stop	
question mark	
speech marks	
comma	
exclamation mark	
colon	
hyphen	
semicolon	
apostrophe	
dash	

In this sentence...

Each of these sentences could be rewritten to contain the types of punctuation shown in the list alongside.

❑ Rewrite the sentences, adding the punctuation shown in the lists.

sara shouted at the top of her voice i won i won

_____

_____

speech marks
exclamation mark
three capital letters
three commas

the room was painted in many colours blue green bright pink and yellow

_____

_____

capital letter
colon
two commas
full stop

sallys coat is lost does anyone know where it is

_____

_____

capital letter
apostrophe
dash
question mark

the fifth of may my birthday is only three days away

_____

_____

two capital letters
full stop
two commas

as the alligator which had escaped from the zoo slipped into the classroom the children shouted help help

_____

_____

capital letter
two exclamation marks
three commas
speech marks

jacks worst nightmare came true when the teacher asked can you sing a solo in assembly

_____

_____

capital letter
apostrophe
question mark
speech marks
comma

Subject knowledge

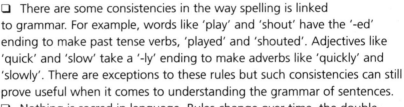

1: Preliminary notes about grammar

Grammar involves the way in which words of different types are combined into sentences. The explanatory sections that follow will include definitions of types of word along with notes on how they are combined into sentences.

Three preliminary points about grammar:

❑ Function is all-important. Where a word is placed in relation to another word is crucial in deciding whether it is functioning as a verb or a noun. For example, the word 'run' will often be thought of as a verb. However, in a sentence like 'They went for a run', the word functions as a noun and the verb is 'went'.

❑ There are some consistencies in the way spelling is linked to grammar. For example, words like 'play' and 'shout' have the '-ed' ending to make past tense verbs, 'played' and 'shouted'. Adjectives like 'quick' and 'slow' take a '-ly' ending to make adverbs like 'quickly' and 'slowly'. There are exceptions to these rules but such consistencies can still prove useful when it comes to understanding the grammar of sentences.

❑ Nothing is sacred in language. Rules change over time, the double negative has gained currency and regional variation in accent and dialect is now far more valued than has been the case in the past. The rules of grammar that follow are subject to change as the language we use lives and grows.

2: Words and functions

Grammar picks out the functions of words. The major classes or types of word in the English language are:

noun

The name of something or someone, including concrete things, such as 'dog' or 'tree', and abstract things, such as 'happiness' or 'fear'.

pronoun

A word that replaces a noun. The noun 'John' in 'John is ill' can be replaced by a pronoun 'he', making 'He is ill'.

verb

A word that denotes an action or a happening. In the sentence 'I ate the cake' the verb is 'ate'. These are sometimes referred to as 'doing' words.

adjective

A word that modifies a noun. In the phrase 'the little boat' the adjective 'little' describes the noun 'boat'.

adverb

A word that modifies a verb. In the phrase 'he slowly walked' the adverb is 'slowly'.

preposition

A word or phrase that shows the relationship of one thing to another. In the phrase 'the house beside the sea' the preposition 'beside' places the two nouns in relation to each other.

conjunction

A word or phrase that joins other words and phrases. A simple example is the word 'and' that joins nouns in 'Snow White and Doc and Sneezy'.

article

The indefinite articles in English are 'a' and 'an' and the definite article is 'the'. Articles appear before nouns and denote whether the noun is specific ('give me the book') or not ('give me a book').

interjection

A word or phrase expressing or exclaiming an emotion, such as 'Oh!' and 'Aaargh!'

The various word types can be found in the following example sentences:

Lou	saw	his	new	house	from	the	train.
noun	verb	pronoun	adjective	noun	preposition	article	noun
Yeow!	I	hit	my	head	on	the	door.
interjection	pronoun	verb	pronoun	noun	preposition	article	noun
Amir	sadly	lost	his	bus fare	down	the	drain.
noun	adverb	verb	pronoun	noun	preposition	article	noun
Give	Jan	a	good	book	for	her	birthday.
verb	noun	article	adjective	noun	conjunction	pronoun	noun

The pages that follow provide more information on these word classes.

Nouns

There are four types of noun in English.

Common nouns are general names for things. For example, in the sentence 'I fed the dog', the noun 'dog' could be used to refer to any dog, not to a specific one. Other examples include 'boy', 'country', 'book', 'apple'.

Proper nouns are the specific names given to identify things or people. In a phrase like 'Sam is my dog' the word 'dog' is the common noun but 'Sam' is a proper noun because it refers to and identifies a specific dog. Other examples include 'the Prime Minister', 'Wales' and 'Amazing Grace'.

Collective nouns refer to a group of things together, such as 'a flock (of sheep)' or 'a bunch (of bananas)'.

A **noun** is the name of someone or something.

Abstract nouns refer to things that are not concrete, such as an action, a concept, an event, quality or state. Abstract nouns like 'happiness' and 'fulfilment' refer to ideas or feelings which are uncountable; others, such as 'hour', 'joke' and 'quantity' are countable.

Nouns can be singular or plural. To change a singular to a plural the usual rule is to add 's'. This table includes other rules to bear in mind, however:

If the singular ends in:	Rule	Examples
'y' after a consonant	Remove 'y', add 'ies'	party → parties
'y' after a vowel	add 's'	donkey → donkeys
'o' after a consonant	add 'es'	potato → potatoes
'o' after a vowel	add 's'	video → videos
a sound like 's', such as 's', 'sh', 'tch', 'x', 'z'	add 'es'	kiss → kisses dish → dishes
		watch → watches
'ch' sounding like it does at the end of 'perch'	add 'es'	church → churches

Pronouns

A **pronoun** is a word that stands in for a noun.

There are different classes of pronoun. The main types are:

Personal pronouns, referring to people or things, such as 'I', 'you', 'it'. The personal pronouns distinguish between subject and object case (I/me, he/him, she/her, we/us, they/them and the archaic thou/thee).

Reflexive pronouns, referring to people or things that are also the subject of the sentence. In the sentence 'You can do this yourself' the pronoun 'yourself' refers to 'you'. Such pronouns end with '-self' or '-selves'. Other examples include 'myself', 'themselves'.

Possessive pronouns identify people or things as belonging to a person or thing. For example, in the sentence 'The book is hers' the possessive pronoun 'hers' refers to 'the book'. Other examples include 'its' and 'yours'. Note that possessive pronouns never take an apostrophe.

Relative pronouns link relative clauses to their nouns. In the sentence 'The man who was in disguise sneaked into the room' the relative clause 'who was in disguise' provides extra information about 'the man'. This relative clause is linked by the relative pronoun 'who'. Other examples include 'whom', 'which' and 'that'.

Interrogative pronouns are used in questions. They refer to the thing that is being asked about. In the question 'What is your name?' and 'Where is the book?' the pronouns 'what' and 'where' stand for the answers – the name and the location of the book.

Demonstrative pronouns are pronouns that 'point'. They are used to show the relation of the speaker to an object. There are four demonstrative pronouns in English: 'this', 'that', 'these', 'those', used as in 'This is my house' and 'That is your house'. They have specific uses, depending upon the position of the object to the speaker:

	Near to speaker	Far away from speaker
Singular	this	that
Plural	these	those

Indefinite pronouns stand in for an indefinite noun. The indefinite element can be the number of elements or the nature of them but they are summed up in ambiguous pronouns such as 'any', 'some' or 'several'. Other examples are the pronouns that end with '-body', '-one' and '-thing', such as 'somebody', 'everyone' and 'anything'.

Person

Personal, reflexive and possessive pronouns can be in the first, second or third person.

First person pronouns (I, we) involve the speaker or writer.

Second person pronouns (you) refer to the listener or reader.

Third person pronouns refer to something other than these two participants in the communication (he, she, it, they).

The person of the pronoun will agree with particular forms of verbs: I like/ She likes.

Verbs

The **tense** of a verb places a happening in time. The main three tenses are the present, past and future.

    To express an action that will take place in the future, verbs appear with 'will' or 'shall' (or 'going to'). The regular past tense is formed by the addition of the suffix '-ed', although some of the most common verbs in English (the 'strong' verbs) have irregular past tenses.

> A **verb** is a word that denotes an action or a happening.

Present tense (happening now)	Past tense (happened in past)	Future tense (to happen in future)
am, say, find, kick	was, said, found, kicked	will be, will say, shall find, shall kick

Continuous verbs

The present participle form of a verb is used to show a continuous action. Whereas a past tense like 'kicked' denotes an action that happened ('I kicked'), the present participle denotes the action as happening and continuing as it is described ('I was kicking', the imperfect tense, or 'I am kicking', the present continuous). There is a sense in these uses of an action that has not ended.

    The present participle usually ends in '-ing', such as 'walking', 'finding', and continuous verbs are made with a form of the verb 'be', such as 'was' or 'am': 'I was running' and 'I am running'.

Subject knowledge

Auxiliary verbs

Auxiliary verbs 'help' other verbs – they regularly accompany full verbs, always preceding them in a verb phrase. The auxiliary verbs in English can be divided into three categories:

Primary verbs are used to indicate the timing of a verb, such as 'be', 'have' or 'did' (including all their variations such as 'was', 'were', 'has', 'had' and so on). These can be seen at work in verb forms like 'I was watching a film', 'He has finished eating', 'I didn't lose my keys'.

Modal verbs indicate the possibility of an action occurring or the necessity of it happening, such as 'I might watch a film', 'I should finish eating' and 'I shouldn't lose my keys'. The modal verbs in English are: would, could, might, should, can, will, shall, may, and must. These verbs never function on their own as main verbs. They always act as auxiliaries helping other verbs.

Marginal modals, namely 'dare', 'need', 'ought to' and 'used to'. These act as modals, such as in the sentences 'I dared enter the room', 'You need to go away' and 'I ought to eat my dinner', but they can also act as main verbs, as in 'I need cake'.

Adjectives

An **adjective** is a word that modifies a noun.

The main function of adjectives is to define quality or quantity. Examples of the use of descriptions of quality include: 'good story', 'sad day' and 'stupid dog'. Examples of the use of descriptions of quantity include 'some stories', 'ten days' and 'many dogs'.

Adjectives can appear in one of three different degrees of intensity. In the table below it can be seen that there are '-er' and '-est' endings that show an adjective is comparative or superlative, though, as can be seen, there are exceptions. The regular comparative is formed by the addition of the suffix '-er' to shorter words and 'more' to longer words (kind/kinder, beautiful/more beautiful). The regular superlative is formed by the addition of the suffix '-est' to shorter words and 'most' to longer words. Note, however, that some common adjectives have irregular comparatives and superlatives.

Nominative The nominative is the plain form that describes a noun.	**Comparative** The comparative implies a comparison between the noun and something else.	**Superlative** The superlative is the ultimate degree of a particular quality.
Examples	**Examples**	**Examples**
long	longer	longest
small	smaller	smallest
big	bigger	biggest
fast	faster	fastest
bad	worse	worst
good	better	best
far	farther/further	farthest/furthest

Adverbs

Adverbs provide extra information about the time, place or manner in which a verb happened.

Manner Provides information about the manner in which the action was done.	Ali *quickly* ran home. The cat climbed *fearfully* up the tree.
Time Provides information about the time at which the action occurred.	*Yesterday* Ali ran home. *Sometimes* the cat climbed up the tree.
Place Provides information about where the action took place.	*Outside* Ali ran home. *In the garden* the cat climbed up the tree.

An **adverb** is a word that modifies a verb.

Variations in the degree of intensity of an adverb are indicated by other adjectives such as 'very', 'rather', 'quite' and 'somewhat'. Comparative forms include 'very quickly', 'rather slowly', and 'most happily'.

The majority of single-word adverbs are made by adding '-ly' to an adjective: 'quick/quickly', 'slow/slowly' and so on.

Prepositions

Prepositions show how nouns or pronouns are positioned in relation to other nouns and pronouns in the same sentence. This can often be the location of one thing in relation to another in space, such as 'on', 'over', 'near'; or time, such as 'before', 'after'.

A **preposition** is a word or phrase that shows the relationship of one thing to another.

Prepositions are usually placed before a noun. They can consist of one word ('The cat *in* the tree...'), two words ('The cat *close to* the gate...') or three ('The cat *on top of* the roof...').

Conjunctions

Conjunctions can join words or clauses in one of four ways:

Name of conjunction	Nature of conjunction	Examples
Addition	One or more things together	We had our tea *and* went out to play. It was a cold day – *also* it rained.
Opposition	One or more things in opposition	I like coffee *but* my brother hates it. It could rain *or* it could snow.
Time	One or more things connected over time	Toby had his tea *then* went out to play. The bus left *before* we reached the stop.
Cause	One or more things causing or caused by another	I took a map *so that* we wouldn't get lost. We got lost *because* we had the wrong map.

A **conjunction** is a word or phrase that joins other words and phrases.

3: Understanding sentences
Types of sentence

The four main types of sentence are **declarative**, **interrogative**, **imperative** and **exclamatory**. The function of a sentence has an effect on the word order; imperatives, for example, often begin with a verb.

Sentence type	Function	Examples
Declarative	Makes a statement	The house is down the lane. Joe rode the bike.
Interrogative	Asks a question	Where is the house? What is Joe doing?
Imperative	Issues a command or direction	Turn left at the traffic lights. Get on your bike!
Exclamatory	Issues an interjection	Wow, what a mess! Oh no!

Sentences: Clauses and complexities
Phrases

A phrase is a set of words performing a grammatical function. In the sentence 'The little, old, fierce dog brutally chased the sad and fearful cat', there are three distinct units performing grammatical functions. The first phrase in this sentence essentially names the dog and provides descriptive information. This is a noun phrase, performing the job of a noun – 'the little, old, fierce dog'. To do this the phrase uses adjectives. The important thing to look out for is the way in which words build around a key word in a phrase. So here the words 'little', 'old' and 'fierce' are built around the word 'dog'. In examples like these, 'dog' is referred to as the **headword** and the adjectives are termed **modifiers**. Together, the modifier and headword make up the noun phrase. Modifiers can also come after the noun, as in 'The little, old, fierce dog that didn't like cats brutally chased the sad and fearful cat'. In this example 'little, 'old' and 'fierce' are **premodifiers** and the phrase 'that didn't like cats' is a **postmodifier**.

The noun phrase is just one of the types of phrase that can be made.

Phrase type	Examples
Noun phrase	The *little, old fierce dog* didn't like cats. She gave him *a carefully and colourfully covered book*.
Verb phrase	The dog *had been hiding* in the house. The man *climbed through* the window without a sound.
Adjectival phrase	The floor was *completely clean*. The floor was *so clean you could eat your dinner off it*.
Adverbial phrase	I finished my lunch *very slowly indeed*. *More confidently than usual*, she entered the room.
Prepositional phrase	The cat sat *at the top of* the tree. The phone rang *in the middle of* the night.

Notice that phrases can appear within phrases. A noun phrase like 'carefully and colourfully covered book' contains the adjectival phrase 'carefully and colourfully covered'. This string of words forms the adjectival phrase in which the words 'carefully' and 'colourfully' modify the adjective 'covered'. Together these words 'carefully and colourfully covered' modify the noun 'book', creating a distinct noun phrase. This is worth noting as it shows how the boundaries between phrases can be blurred, a fact that can cause confusion unless borne in mind!

Clauses

Clauses are units of meaning included within a sentence, usually containing a verb and other elements linked to it. 'The burglar ran' is a clause containing the definite article, noun and verb; 'The burglar quickly ran from the little house' is also a clause that adds an adverb, preposition and adjective. The essential element in a clause is the verb. Clauses look very much like small sentences, indeed sentences can be constructed of just one clause: 'The burglar hid', 'I like cake'.

Sentences can also be constructed out of a number of clauses linked together: 'The burglar ran and I chased him because he stole my cake.' This sentence contains three clauses: 'The burglar ran', 'I chased him', 'he stole my cake'.

Clauses and phrases: the difference

Clauses include participants in an action denoted by a verb. Phrases, however, need not necessarily contain a verb. These phrases make little sense on their own: 'without a sound', 'very slowly indeed'. They work as part of a clause.

Simple, compound and complex sentences

The addition of clauses can make complex or compound sentences.

Simple sentences are made up of one clause, for example: 'The dog barked', 'Sam was scared'.

Compound sentences are made up of clauses added to clauses. In compound sentences each of the clauses is of equal value; no clause is dependent on another. An example of a compound sentence is: 'The dog barked and the parrot squawked'. Both these clauses are of equal importance: 'The dog barked', 'the parrot squawked'.

Other compound sentences include, for example: 'I like coffee and I like chocolate', 'I like coffee, but I don't like tea'.

Complex sentences are made up of a main clause with a subordinate clause or clauses. Subordinate clauses make sense in relation to the main clause. They say something about it and are dependent upon it, for example in the sentences:
'The dog barked because he saw a burglar', 'Sam was scared so he phoned the police'.

In both these cases the subordinate clause ('he saw a burglar', 'he phoned the police') is elaborating on the main clause. They explain why the dog barked or why Sam was scared and, in doing so, are subordinate to those actions. The reader needs to see the main clauses to fully appreciate what the subordinate ones are stating.

Subject and object

The **subject** of a sentence or clause is the agent that performs the action denoted by the verb – '*Shaun* threw the ball'. The **object** is the agent to which the verb is done – 'ball'. It could be said that the subject does the verb to the object (a simplification but a useful one). The simplest type of sentence is known as the SVO (subject–verb–object) sentence (or clause), as in 'You lost your way', 'I found the book' and 'Lewis met Chloe'.

The active voice and the passive voice

These contrast two ways of saying the same thing:

Active voice	Passive voice
I found the book. Megan met Ben. The cow jumped over the moon.	The book was found by me. Ben was met by Megan. The moon was jumped over by the cow.

The two types of clause put the same subject matter in a different **voice**. Passive clauses are made up of a subject and verb followed by an agent.

The book	was found by	me.
subject	verb	agent
Ben	was met by	Megan.
subject	verb	agent

Sentences can be written in the active or the passive voice. A sentence can be changed from the active to the passive voice by:

❑ moving the subject to the end of the clause
❑ moving the object to the start of the clause
❑ changing the verb or verb phrase by placing a form of the verb 'be' before it (as in 'was found')
❑ changing the verb or verb phrase by placing 'by' after it.

In passive clauses the agent can be deleted, either because it does not need mentioning or because a positive choice is made to omit it. Texts on science may leave out the agent, with sentences such as 'The water is added to the salt and stirred'.

4: Punctuation

Punctuation provides marks within sentences that guide the reader. Speech doesn't need punctuation (and would sound bizarre if it included noises for full stops etc). In speech, much is communicated by pausing, changing tone and so on. In writing, the marks within and around a sentence provide indications of when to pause, when something is being quoted and so on.

Punctuation mark	Uses	Examples
A	**Capital letter** 1. Start a sentence. 2. Indicate proper nouns. 3. Emphasize certain words.	All I want is cake. You can call me Al. I want it TOMORROW!
.	**Full stop** Ends sentences that are not questions or exclamations.	This is a sentence.
?	**Question mark** Ends a sentence that is a question.	Is this a question?
!	**Exclamation mark** Ends a sentence that is an exclamation.	Don't do that!
" " ' '	**Quotation (speech) marks (or inverted commas)** Enclose direct speech. Can be double or single.	"Help me," the man yelled. 'Help me,' the man yelled.
,	**Comma** 1. Places a pause between clauses within a sentence. 2. Separates items in a list. 3. Separates adjectives in a series. 4. Completely encloses clauses inserted in a sentence. 5. Marks speech from words denoting who said them.	We were late, although it didn't matter. You will need eggs, butter, salt and flour. I wore a long, green, frilly skirt. We were, after we had rushed to get there, late for the film. 'Thank you,' I said.
–	**Hyphen** Connects elements of certain words.	Co-ordinator, south-west.
:	**Colon** 1. Introduces lists (including examples).	To go skiing these are the main items you will need: a hat, gloves, goggles and sunscreen.

continued...

Punctuation mark	Uses	Examples
	2. Introduces summaries. 3. Introduces (direct) quotations. 4. Introduces a second clause that expands or illustrates the meaning of the first.	We have learned the following on the ski slope: do a snow plough to slow down… My instructor always says: 'Bend those knees.' The snow hardened: it turned into ice.
;	**Semicolon** 1. Separates two closely linked clauses, and shows there is a link between them. 2. Separates items in a complex list.	On Tuesday, the bus was late; the train was early. You can go by aeroplane, train and taxi; Channel tunnel train, coach, then a short walk; or aeroplane and car.
'	**Apostrophe of possession** Denotes the ownership of one thing by another (see page 160).	This is Mona's scarf. These are the teachers' books.
'	**Apostrophe of contraction** Shows the omission of a letter(s) when two (or occasionally more) words are contracted.	Don't walk on the grass.
•••	**Ellipsis** 1. Shows the omission of words. 2. Indicates a pause.	The teacher moaned, 'Look at this floor… a mess… this class…' Lou said: 'I think I locked the door… no, hang on, did I?'
( )	**Brackets** Contains a parenthesis – a word or phrase added to a sentence to give a bit more information.	The cupboard (which had been in my family for years) was broken.
—	**Dash** 1. Indicates additional information, with more emphasis than a comma. 2. Indicates a pause, especially for effect at the end of a sentence. 3. Contains extra information (used instead of brackets).	She is a teacher – and a very good one too. We all know what to expect – the worst. You finished that job – and I don't know how – before the deadline.

Subject knowledge

Adding an apostrophe of possession

The addition of an apostrophe can create confusion. The main thing to look at is the noun – ask:

- ❑ Is it singular or plural?
- ❑ Does it end in an 's'?

If the noun is singular and doesn't end in 's', you add an apostrophe and an 's', for example: Indra's house the firefighter's bravery	If the noun is singular and ends in 's', you add an apostrophe and an 's', for example: the bus's wheels Thomas's pen
If the noun is plural and doesn't end in 's', you add an apostrophe and an 's', for example: the women's magazine the geese's flight	If the noun is plural and ends in 's', you add an apostrophe but don't add an 's', for example: the boys' clothes the dancers' performance

Further reading

Carter, R; Goddard, A; Reah, D; Sanger, K; Bowring, K (1997) *Working with Texts: A Core Book for Language Analysis*, Routledge

Crystal, D (1988) *Rediscover Grammar with David Crystal*, Longman

Crystal, D (1995) *The Cambridge Encyclopedia of the English Language*, Cambridge University Press
A big volume but very accessible, covering many areas of English including grammar, punctuation and dialect. Filled with interesting asides and examples from sources as varied as Shakespeare to Monty Python.

Hurford, R (1994) *Grammar: A student's guide*, Cambridge University Press
An excellent text, setting out basic guidelines on the workings of grammar.

Reah, D and Ross, A (1997) *Exploring Grammar: Main Routes and Scenic Paths*, WordsWork
A popular and accessible introductory course to grammar with interesting exercises to guide the reader.

Sealey, A (1996) *Learning About Language: Issues for Primary Teachers*, Open University Press
A more theoretical work that presents some of the issues and arguments surrounding knowledge about language.